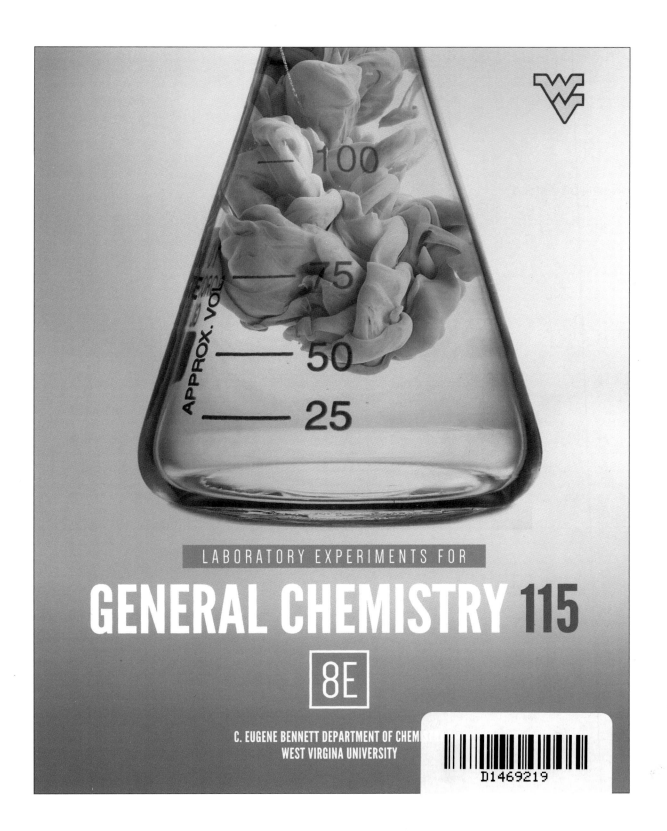

LABORATORY EXPERIMENTS FOR

GENERAL CHEMISTRY 115

8E

C. EUGENE BENNETT DEPARTMENT OF CHEMIS...
WEST VIRGINA UNIVERSITY

D1469219

bluedoor
flexible & affordable learning solutions™

Chief Executive Officer: Jon K. Earl

President, College: Lucas Tomasso
President, Private Sector: Dawn Earl

Print Solutions Manager: Connie Dayton
Digital Solutions Manager: Amber Wahl
Senior Project Coordinator: Dan Woods
Senior Project Coordinator: Peggy Li
Project Coordinator: Erica Rieck
Project Coordinator: Kelli Fleck
Project Coordinator: Shannon VanHouten
Production Assistant: Stephanie Larson
Production Assistant: Jessie Steigauf

Cover Design: Dan Woods

ISBN-13: 978-1-68135-405-7

Published by bluedoor, LLC
          10949 Bren Road East
          Minneapolis, MN 55343-9613
          800-979-1624
          www.bluedoorpublishing.com

Printed in the United States of America.
10 9 8 7 6 5 4 3 2

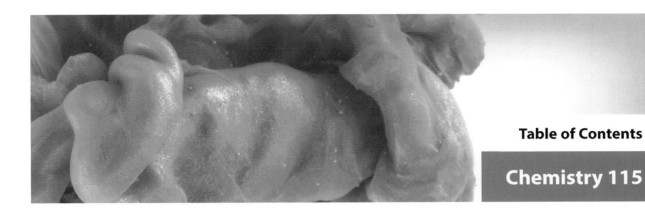

Table of Contents

Chemistry 115

Introduction

Experiment 1

Experiment 2

Experiment 3

Experiment 4

Experiment 5

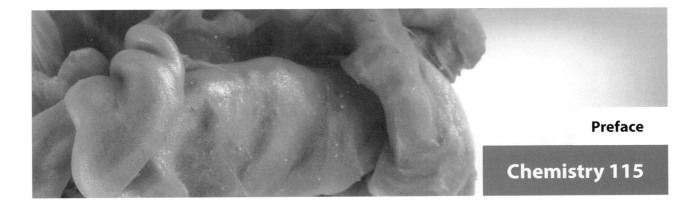

Preface

Chemistry 115

In studying introductory chemistry, the student is introduced to many theoretical concepts based on conclusions drawn from many years of accumulated observations. Since it is often difficult to appreciate the importance of experimental observation and its relationship to theory, this laboratory manual was designed to provide the student with exposure to the basic techniques of laboratory work as well as practical experience necessary to understand and appreciate laboratory data and how it relates to theory.

Each experiment includes objectives, experimental procedures, and data report sheets. Emphasis is placed on experimental precision, obtaining accurate results, and further developing and expanding chemical knowledge through experimentation. In addition, each experiment seeks to provide relevance and answer the oft-asked student question, "What is the value of learning chemistry?"

The original version of this manual, which has been often modified and altered as necessary to keep up with modern trends in chemical education, was the result of the timeless efforts of Professors J. L. Hall, A. D. Paul, and Peter Popovich. This version of the laboratory manual was developed with significant input from Professors E. Battin, R. Nakon, B. Ratcliff, M. Xu, and M. Richards-Babb with contributions from R. J. Sweeney and M. W. Vannatta and with many functional suggestions from our Teaching Assistants. The present version of the manual is dedicated to the above-mentioned for their many contributions to the freshman chemistry program at West Virginia University.

THE WEST VIRGINIA UNIVERSITY CHEMISTRY STAFF

To the Student

Prior to each laboratory period, you should study the experiment that has been assigned and become familiar with the work to be done. Your work should be planned so that it may be completed within the assigned time. Arrive at your laboratory room on time. Should you complete your work before the end of the period, check with your laboratory Teaching Assistant and obtain approval of your experimental work before leaving the laboratory room.

You are not to work in the laboratory at times other than the period for which you are regularly scheduled. If because of illness or unavoidable absence it is necessary to work at some other time, you must obtain permission from your instructor.

Feel free to ask questions of your laboratory Teaching Assistant or instructor.

At the end of each laboratory period, clean all glassware and return all equipment to your laboratory drawer. Return all common equipment (Bunsen burners, tubing, clamps, handheld probeware units) to the common equipment container or storage shelving. Clean your workspace (use a wet sponge) and the sink that serves your area. Check to make sure the water and gas are turned off.

Answers to questions are to be written in the spaces provided on the data report sheets. Record all data and results at the time the work is performed. Never record results on loose scraps of paper. In experiments involving calculations, a neat sample calculation should be shown. Although neatness is desirable, it is secondary to working out all answers in the laboratory manual at the time the laboratory work is done. Data report sheets are to be handed in at the end of the laboratory period for grading.

Laboratory Glassware and Equipment

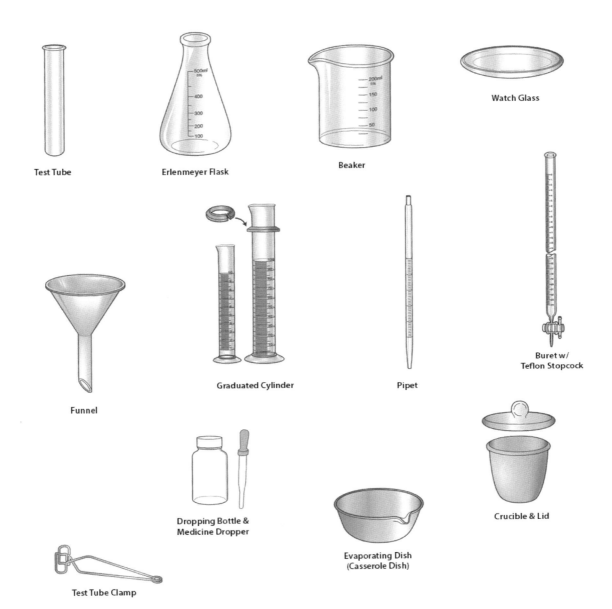

Test Tube

Erlenmeyer Flask

Beaker

Watch Glass

Funnel

Graduated Cylinder

Pipet

Buret w/
Teflon Stopcock

Dropping Bottle &
Medicine Dropper

Evaporating Dish
(Casserole Dish)

Crucible & Lid

Test Tube Clamp

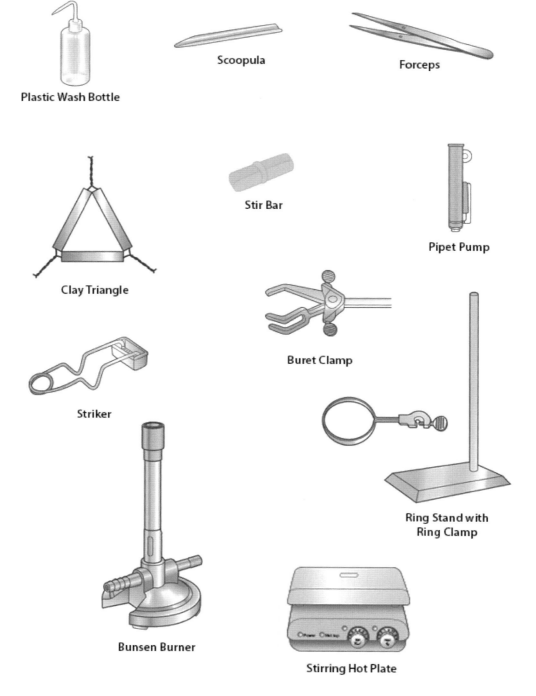

Plastic Wash Bottle

Scoopula

Forceps

Clay Triangle

Stir Bar

Pipet Pump

Striker

Buret Clamp

Bunsen Burner

Ring Stand with
Ring Clamp

Stirring Hot Plate

Safety Rules for Undergraduate Students in Chemistry Laboratories

EBERLY COLLEGE OF ARTS AND SCIENCES

C. EUGENE BENNETT DEPARTMENT OF CHEMISTRY

MARCH 2010

The following guidelines and policies are designed to protect students from exposure to hazardous chemicals in the academic laboratories. According to the Occupational Safety and Health Administration definition, a hazardous chemical is a chemical for which there is statistically significant evidence, based on at least one study conducted in accordance with established scientific principles, that acute or chronic health effects may occur in exposed persons. The safety rules will be enforced at all times by authorized departmental personnel. Students who do not follow the safety rules will be subject to dismissal from the laboratory.

I. Guidelines for Personal Apparel in the Laboratory

A. Students must wear approved chemical splash goggles (over regular eyeglasses) and approved laboratory aprons or cotton lab coats (not lab jackets) at all times in the laboratory.

B. The use of contact lenses in the laboratory is strongly discouraged. In the event of a chemical splash or vapor release, contact lenses can increase the degree of injury to the eye and may prevent prompt first-aid and eye-flushing procedures.

C. Students should wear cotton clothing that provides protection from chemical spills. Clothing that completely covers the legs must be worn at all times in the laboratory. Shorts and skirts that do not completely cover the legs are inappropriate apparel in the laboratory and *are not permitted.*

D. To avoid exposure to hazardous materials, open-backed shirts, bare midriff shirts, or shirts that expose areas of the torso *are not permitted.*

E. Wear shoes that completely cover the feet. Sandals, perforated shoes, open-toed shoes, open-backed shoes, or high-heeled shoes are not permitted in the laboratory.

F. For your safety, hair longer than shoulder length and loose sleeves must be confined when working in the laboratory.

G. Wear the disposable gloves that are provided in each laboratory when working with hazardous chemicals. Inspect the gloves for defects before wearing. Be sure to notify your Teaching Assistant if you have an allergy to latex. Always remove gloves before exiting the laboratory. Upon removal, discard the disposable gloves in the wastebasket.

H. You are advised to avoid wearing synthetic fingernails in the chemistry laboratory. Synthetic finger-nails can be damaged by solvents and are made of extremely flammable polymers, which can burn to completion and are not easily extinguished.

I. For your protection, jewelry should not be worn in the laboratory. Dangling jewelry can become entangled in equipment and can conduct electricity. Chemicals can seep under the jewelry and cause injuries to the skin. Chemicals can ruin jewelry and change its composition.

II. Procedures to Avoid Exposure to Hazardous Chemicals

A. Minimize all chemical exposure. Avoid ingestion, injection, inhalation, eye contact, and skin contact with all hazardous materials in the laboratory.

B. No chemical should ever be tasted. Do not pipet by mouth in the laboratory; use a pipet aid.

C. When you are instructed to smell a chemical, you should gently waft the vapors toward your nose using your gloved hand or a folded sheet of paper. Do not place the container directly under your nose and inhale the vapors.

D. Use the chemical fume hood when there is a possibility of release of toxic chemical vapors, dust, or gases. Before you begin your experimental work in the general chemistry laboratories, always ensure that the back of the desktop fume hood is properly aligned with the ventilation duct that is located on the benchtop at each student desk. When using a chemical fume hood that has a sash, the sash opening should be kept at a minimum to protect the user and to ensure the efficiency of the operation. Keep your head and body outside of the hood face. All chemicals and equipment should be placed at least six inches from the hood face to ensure proper airflow.

E. If any chemical spills onto the skin, immediately flush the affected area with water and notify the Teaching Assistant.

F. Eating, drinking, smoking, chewing gum, applying cosmetics, and using smokeless tobacco products are prohibited in the laboratory. Beverage containers, cups, bottled water, and food containers are not permitted in the laboratory. Never use laboratory glassware for eating or drinking purposes.

G. Always remove gloves before exiting the laboratory. Dispose of gloves in a wastebasket, not in the solid waste container. Do not reuse gloves.

H. Notify your Teaching Assistant if you spill any chemicals. Clean up chemical spills (including water) immediately. Do not leave spilled chemicals on the benchtop or floor. At the termination of your experimental work, the desktop and student hood must be thoroughly cleaned before you leave the laboratory. The Teaching Assistant will advise you of the proper manner to dispose of the cleaning materials.

I. Notify the Teaching Assistant about any sensitivities that you may have to particular chemicals prior to the start of the particular laboratory experiment.

J. Due to possible contamination of laboratory coats with chemicals, students are advised that they should not wear laboratory coats outside of the Chemistry buildings and that they should not wash laboratory coats with personal clothing items.

K. Always wash your hands at the end of each laboratory session before you exit the laboratory.

III. General Guidelines for Laboratory Procedures

A. Do not enter the laboratory room without the supervision of your Teaching Assistant or the faculty member in charge of the laboratory. Working in the laboratory without supervision by the Teaching Assistant or the faculty member in charge is prohibited. The performance of unauthorized experiments and the use of any equipment in an unauthorized or unsafe manner are strictly forbidden.

B. When diluting concentrated acids, *always* pour the acid slowly into the water with stirring. Never add water to concentrated acids because of the danger of splattering.

C. When cutting glass tubing, always protect your hands with a towel. When inserting rods, tubing, or thermometers into stoppers, the glass must be lubricated with soapy water or glycerol. Tubing ends must always be fire-polished. Make sure that the glass is cool before you touch it. Hot glass looks just like cool glass.

D. Do not attempt to dry glassware by inserting a towel wrapped around a glass rod.

E. Glass tubing should extend well through rubber stoppers so that no closure of the tube can occur if the rubber swells.

F. All water, gas, air, electrical, and other service connections must be made in a safe and secure manner.

G. Practical jokes, boisterous conduct, and excessive noise are prohibited.

H. The use of personal audio and visual equipment and cell phones is prohibited in the laboratory.

I. Gas valves must be kept closed except when a burner is in use.

J. Do not heat flammable liquids with a Bunsen burner or other open flame. If in doubt about the flammability of a liquid, consult your Teaching Assistant.

K. Dispose of waste chemicals in the containers that have been provided and labeled for this purpose. Do not dispose of waste chemicals in the sinks or the wastebaskets. Paper towels and gloves should be placed in the wastebasket, not the chemical waste containers. Used filter paper and weighing dishes must be placed in the containers that are marked for this purpose.

L. Examine all apparatus for defects before performing any experiments. Do not use damaged, cracked, or otherwise defective glassware. Dispose of broken glassware in the containers provided in the laboratory.

M. If you break a thermometer (or find a broken thermometer), report it to your Teaching Assistant immediately.

N. Do not insert medicine droppers into reagent bottles unless they are specifically supplied with the bottles.

O. Never return unused chemicals to the stock reagent bottles. Take only what you need. Use the quantities of reagents recommended in your laboratory manual. Do not waste chemicals.

P. Do not remove stock reagent bottles from the dispensing areas without the permission of the Teaching Assistant or the instructor.

Q. All materials (i.e., chemicals, paper towels, broken glass, stoppers, and rubber tubing) must be kept out of the sinks at all times to minimize the danger of plugging drains. Such items are to be kept away from positions where they might fall into the sinks or drains.

R. Maintain clean glassware. When cleaning glassware with water, wash your equipment with tap water. Use distilled water only for rinsing. Do not use more distilled water than is necessary. Ethanol and acetone rinses must be placed in the appropriately labeled container in the laboratory, as instructed by the Teaching Assistant.

S. Heavy pieces of glass apparatus and filter flasks should be supported with clamps suitably protected with rubber or plastic pads. Heavy pieces of glass apparatus that are not sitting directly on the bench-top should have appropriate bottom supports, such as rings or tripods.

T. Coats, bags, and other personal items should be stored in the proper areas, not on the benchtops or in the aisleways.

U. When heating or carrying out a reaction in a test tube, never point the test tube toward your neighbor or yourself.

V. All containers containing chemicals or solutions of any kind that are retained between laboratory sessions *must* be labeled so that the contents can be identified by chemistry personnel. The label must also contain the date and the name of the responsible person.

W. Caps must be kept firmly in place on all reagent bottles and waste containers when not in use.

X. Return all of your equipment and glassware to your student drawer. Lock your drawer at the end of each laboratory session.

Y. At the end of the laboratory session, return all common equipment to the common equipment drawer. Do not place the common equipment in your assigned student drawer.

IV. Departmental and Institutional Laboratory Policies

A. When the fire alarm sounds you must evacuate the building via the nearest exit. Extinguish all flames and turn off all equipment, as appropriate, before exiting.

B. All personal injuries and illnesses, however slight, occurring in the laboratory must be reported immediately to the Teaching Assistant in charge of the laboratory.

C. Report any accident (i.e., personal injury, fire, explosion, chemical spill, or the breaking of equipment) to your Teaching Assistant immediately.

D. No chemical should ever be poured down the laboratory drains or placed in the wastebaskets. Properly dispose of all waste chemicals in the containers that have been provided in the laboratories.

E. Visitors, including children and pets, are not permitted to enter laboratory rooms.

F. As a reminder of institutional policy, smoking is prohibited in all chemistry laboratories.

G. Do not take laboratory equipment, glassware, or chemicals from the laboratory room without the permission of the Teaching Assistant.

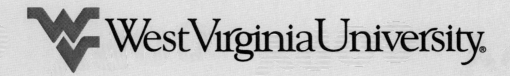

WestVirginiaUniversity®

Eberly College of Arts and Sciences

C. Eugene Bennett Department of Chemistry

SAFETY RULES FOR UNDERGRADUATE STUDENTS
IN CHEMISTRY LABORATORIES

I have read and I understand the Safety Rules for Undergraduate Students in Chemistry Laboratories issued by the Department of Chemistry at West Virginia University. In consideration of being allowed to take this course, I will abide by these guidelines and policies.

_____   _____
Student Signature   Date

_____
Name (print)

_____
Student ID Number

_____
Course Number

_____
Room Number

_____
Desk Number

_____   _____
Teaching Assistant Signature   Date

Return this completed form to your Teaching Assistant.
This form will be maintained as a permanent record of this course.

Revised Nov. 1995, Jan. 2000, May 2002, May 2004, Feb. 2009, March 2010

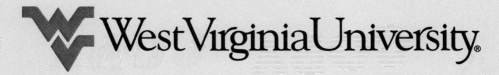

C. Eugene Bennett Department of Chemistry

USE OF CONTACT LENSES IN CHEMISTRY LABORATORY

SAFETY GOGGLES WITH SHIELDED VENTS ONLY MUST BE WORN AT ALL TIMES IN CHEMISTRY LABORATORIES WHEN WEARING CONTACT LENSES. Such safety goggles prevent liquids or solid particles from being splashed or sprayed into the eyes and they reduce contact with laboratory vapors. Gases and vapors can concentrate under the contact lenses and cause permanent eye damage. It has been shown that soft contact lenses can pose an even greater risk of vapor absorption and possible eye damage than hard contact lenses. In addition to the possible vapor and gas hazards, contact lenses may trap foreign matter in the eye and produce abrasion of the cornea. Contact lens wearers are advised to remove their contact lenses and replace them with conventional eyeglasses before coming to the Chemistry laboratory, when possible, to avoid the possibility of the aforementioned hazards as well as any unforeseen problems that might occur as a result of wearing contact lenses. The exceptions to this general rule include persons who cannot wear corrective glasses for medical reasons or persons for whom contact lenses are medically required for therapeutic reasons.

RELEASE IN FULL OF ALL CLAIMS

I have read and understand the information set out above pertaining to the potential risks of wearing contact lenses in the Chemistry laboratory.

In consideration of being permitted to participate in the laboratory course, I agree to wear safety goggles at ALL times in the laboratory and to notify my Teaching Assistant that I am wearing contact lenses each time I enter the laboratory wearing such lenses.

I fully understand that I assume FULL RESPONSIBILITY for any injury that might occur as a result of or connected in any way to the fact that I wear contact lenses in the Chemistry laboratory.

_____

Printed Name

_____ _____

Chemistry Course   Section Number

_____ _____

Room Number   Desk Number

_____ _____

Student Signature   Date

_____ _____

Witness Signature   Date

August 2010

Return this completed form to your Teaching Assistant.
This form will be maintained as a permanent record of this course.

Chem 115 Safety Assignment

Instructions: Use complete sentences to answer questions 3–14. Please use the "Safety Rules for Undergraduate Students in Chemistry Laboratories" to help you answer each question.

1. Sketch below a representation of your laboratory, showing clearly the location of the following: exits, fire extinguisher, safety shower, eyewash fountain, student hood, and fire blanket.

2. Determine whether each of the following items of apparel or footwear are forbidden (F), unsafe (U), or appropriate (A) for Chemistry laboratory.

    A. sandals
    B. long pants
    C. high-heeled shoess
    D. synthetic fingernails
    E. contact lenses
    F. safety goggles
    G. shorts
    H. long-sleeve T-shirts

    I. clogs
    J. long skirts (ankle length)
    K. short skirts or dresse
    L. dangling necklaces
    M. safety glasses
    N. laboratory aprons
    O. sandals with socks underneath
    P. sneakers

3. What is considered the "best" attire for chemistry laboratory?

4. What is the correct way to "smell" a chemical?

5. A chemical reaction is known to be accompanied by the release of a noxious gas. Where should this chemical reaction be carried out?

6. An acid spills onto your skin. What should you do?

7. After use, where should latex gloves and paper towels be disposed? Waste chemicals? Broken glassware?

8. A concentrated acid is to be diluted with water. Should the water be added to the acid or should the acid be added to the water? Why?

9. A 5-mL portion of a chemical is needed, but you accidentally dispense 20 mL of the chemical into a beaker. Should the excess chemical be poured back into the reagent bottle? Why or why not? Where should you dispose of excess chemical?

10. The heating of a chemical is carried out in an open test tube. Where should you point the mouth of the test tube?

11. In the middle of your experiment, the fire alarm sounds. What should you do?

12. You are wearing latex gloves because you are working with concentrated NaOH. However, you have used up all of your chemical unknown and need to go to the third floor prep room to get more unknown. What should you do with your gloves? Why?

13. While pouring a chemical, you accidently spill some of the chemical on the laboratory benchtop. It seems to dry, so, you never clean it up. That afternoon, a student leans his arm on the same spot and notices the appearance of a red, burning welt. Who is at fault? What could you have done to avert this situation?

14. Although your Teaching Assistant told you that pouring of chemicals near/on the precision electronic balances (>$1,000 each) was forbidden, you did it anyway. Although you were "careful," you did spill some chemical onto the electronic balance but neglected to clean it up. The following week, you notice (i) a sign on the balance that says "Do not use. Broken!" (ii) rust marks on the electronic balance, and (iii) long lines to use the remaining electronic balances. Who is at fault? How could this situation have been avoided?

SPARK™ Unit Tutorial

This tutorial has been assembled for you to become more familiar with the SPARK units that are currently being used within the General Chemistry laboratory curriculum. The SPARK Science Learning System is an all-in-one mobile device that seamlessly integrates the power of probeware with inquiry-based content and assessment. With its large, full-color display; finger-touch navigation; and data collection and analysis capabilities, SPARK redefines the concept of easy-to-use. Nevertheless, a short tutorial will help you in working with the SPARK unit.

- *Obtain a SPARK unit and temperature sensor from your Teaching Assistant and identify the features discussed below.*

Figure 0.1 displays photos of the SPARK unit with its basic external features. The area marked with a (1) is the AC adapter port whereas (2) is the power button. Each SPARK unit has the ability to run on batteries but will be plugged into AC power sources during your experiments. The SPARK unit is turned on by pressing the power button (2) for a couple of seconds. The areas labeled with (3) are Pasport sensor ports. A sensor is a device that detects and responds to a signal. Most sensors are made as slender instruments or "probes." There are a variety of sensors or probes that are compatible and can be used with the SPARK units. These sensors can be directly plugged into the SPARK unit as seen in *Figure 0.1* or they are connected via adapter cables. The input labeled (4) is the temperature sensor input while the input labeled (5) is the voltage input.

Figure 0.1: Photograph of the SPARK unit and its external features.[1]

---

1 Screenshots are of SPARKvue™, and the hardware images are of the SPARK Science Learning System™ and PASPORT® Light Sensor from PASCO scientific.

- *Plug in and turn on the SPARK unit.*

The SPARK unit will turn on after a few seconds of software loading. If no sensors are currently connected, the home screen will appear as in *Figure 0.2*. At this point, one may either build or open an existing application. However, these features are beyond the scope of this tutorial. Currently, all of the experiments that utilize the SPARK unit do not require customization of the units.

Figure 0.2: The home screen of the SPARK unit as it looks
when no sensors are plugged in.

The home screen will change as soon as a sensor is plugged into the SPARK unit. The software within the SPARK unit automatically recognizes and displays the proper screen depending on the sensor that is plugged in. *Figure 0.3* illustrates an example of sensor recognition. In this case, a general science sensor has been plugged into the SPARK unit. This particular sensor simultaneously displays four readings: sound level, voltage, temperature, and light intensity. At this point you can do one of two things: monitor all sensor readings from the home page or select a single sensor for more specific interrogation. Notice that only one-half of the screen is displayed. This is because only one sensor port is currently occupied. Recall *Figure 0.1*. There are two different multifunctional sensor ports that can both be utilized. If we were to plug in another general science sensor into the other port, then the other half of the screen would appear identical but would be displaying data from the additional sensor.

Figure 0.3: Home screen of SPARK unit once a sensor has been recognized.

- *Plug in the temperature sensor into port #4 of your SPARK unit. The SPARK unit will recognize the sensor and display a home screen similar to Figure 0.3.*

- *Squeeze the end of the temperature sensor for ca. 15 seconds and observe the change in temperature on the display.*

- *Select the temperature sensor by touching the temperature display. The display will then become highlighted in orange (Figure 0.4).*

Figure 0.4: Home screen of SPARK unit once a sensor has been selected.

- *Once the temperature display is highlighted in orange, touch the show button. The show button is located in the middle along the bottom of the home screen.*

- *The SPARK unit will now display the SPARK lab screen page (Figure 0.5). This page is where the many utilities of the SPARK unit really come into play. This screen is the user's interface to start, stop, and record data collection.*

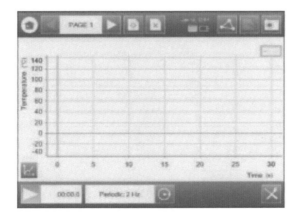

Figure 0.5: SPARK lab screen page.

- *Press the (green) button located in the lower-left part of the screen. Once selected, the button changes to an orange color. This button starts data collection. You will now notice the real-time plotting of data points on the SPARK lab screen page (Figure 0.6).*

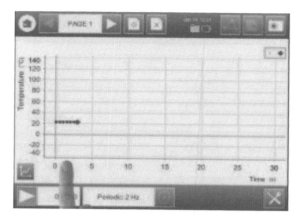

Figure 0.6: Real-time data collection as displayed on the SPARK lab screen page.

- *The SPARK unit has the ability to display the data in a number of ways. Press the arrow button located to the right of "Page 1" in the upper-left part of the screen. You will then go to "Page 2," which is a digital display of the real-time data collection. Proceeding further takes you to "Page 3," the table view. An analog meter display is visible once you reach "Page 4." Figure 0.7 illustrates the various data display pages.*

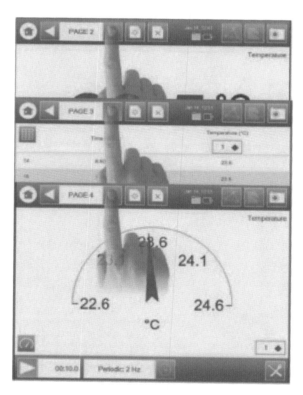

Figure 0.7: Views of the other pages available when recording and/or displaying data with the SPARK unit.

- *Play around a bit with the data display pages while you continue to collect data with your temperature probe.*

- *Once you are satisfied with your ability to view data collection, place the temperature probe in the palm of your hand and squeeze.*

- *Using the other hand, play around again with the data display pages so you can view the real-time increase in temperature provided by the heat from your hand.*

- *After a couple of minutes of raising the temperature with your hand, press the (orange) button to stop data collection. Proceed back to the "Page 1" data display page (the graph).*

- *The temperature change that has occurred is difficult to view because of the scale of the graph (Figure 0.8).*

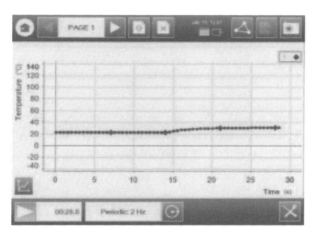

Figure 0.8: Screen shot displaying a temperature increase that is difficult to see based upon the scale.

- *There are various ways in which you can manipulate the view of the data once you have finished a data collection "run."*

- *The first way is to simply touch and drag your finger around the screen in the areas around your data points. Give this a try with your data. Be patient! It takes a second or two for the SPARK unit to respond.*

- *The second way is to touch and drag your finger along the axes of the graph. Dragging toward the top of the page on the y-axis will expand the y scale. Similarly, dragging toward the right of the screen on the x-axis will expand the x scale. Performing opposite tasks will contract the scales.*

- *Even more functions are available via the graph button, . Press the graph button to get a new set of buttons to appear on the right-hand side of the graph. Touch the button in the top right corner, . This is the autoscale button and will automatically scale the displayed data to fit your screen. Your data should now look similar to that displayed in Figure 0.9.*

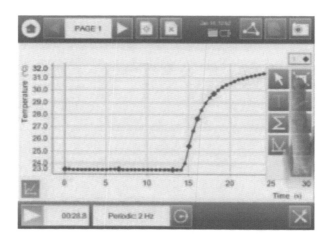

Figure 0.9: Data view once the autoscale button is enabled.

- *The autoscale button definitely makes viewing the data easier. However, oftentimes you will only be interested in a certain portion of the data. In that case, you need to engage the select button, .*

To use the select button, simply touch the screen on two different sides of the data. A red-colored box will then appear, which will further let you control which specific data points you wish to investigate (Figure 0.10). The two smaller red boxes with the arrows inside allow you to fine-tune the selection of your data. Be sure to press the "OK" button once you have tweaked the selection box. Play around with the selection of your data. In addition, once you have selected the data you want to further investigate, you can again use the autoscale button, , to make it fit the screen.

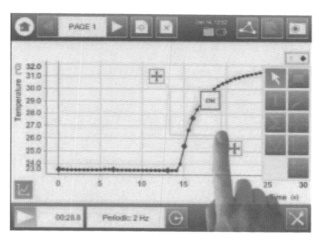

Figure 0.10: Use of the select button allows you to further investigate smaller portions of the data.

- *Additionally, you may choose to investigate only one data point. Use the select button,* ▣ *,and touch on or near the data point you wish to investigate. Once you have done this, a new text box appears above the graph to the left. The text box is flanked by arrow buttons. The text box displays the x and y-coordinates for the various data points you are currently investigating. Hit the arrow buttons and notice how the text box changes as you proceed either up or down your data line. When you are finished, press the OK button.*

- *Press the (green)* ▶ *button again to start a new run. Place the temperature probe in the palm of your hand. While you are still collecting data, press the* ▣ *button. Now press the autoscale button,* ▣ *, which will allow you to autoscale your data collection in real time. When you are finished playing around with the various buttons during data collection, press the (orange)* ▶ *button to terminate the run.*

- *You will now notice a legend in the upper-right portion of the graph. This legend displays the symbols representing the two runs you just performed. Touch the legend. You are now able to select and/or deselect one of the runs. Play around with this feature for a bit. The SPARK unit allows you to do multiple runs and then compare them all or investigate them separately.*

This short tutorial should make you more familiar with the SPARK unit's operation and functions. You will be using the SPARK unit throughout the semester as you complete various laboratory experiments. Although we only utilized the temperature sensor for this tutorial, other sensors are very similar in operation.

- *The last task for you to do is to exit to the home screen. Touch the home screen button,* ▣ *, in the upper-left part of the screen. This button will take you back to the home screen after it asks you whether you want to save your data. Select the "No" option for data saving and proceed to the home screen. Going to the home screen will always clear the memory of the SPARK unit.* **Warning! Only proceed to the home screen if you need to erase an experiment and/or sensor calibration.**

- *Finally, push the power button for a couple of seconds until the SPARK unit powers down.*

Experiment 1

Synthesis of Nanoparticles: Ferrofluids

SAFETY PRECAUTIONS

- Chemical splash goggles, gloves, and apron must be worn at all times.
- Magnetite solutions permanently stain clothing. Avoid contact of chemicals with clothing and skin.
- Acid and base solutions are caustic and corrosive. Immediately wash all spills with excess water and inform the teaching assistant.
- $Nd_2Fe_{12}B$ magnets strongly attract to metal surfaces and other magnets. Placing one magnet on top of another is not recommended and poses a pinching hazard.

Materials List

- iron(III)chloride, $FeCl_3$
- iron(II)chloride tetrahydrate, $FeCl_2 \cdot 4H_2O$
- 10 M ammonia, NH_3
- cyclohexane, C_6H_{12}
- 13,000 Gauss $Nd_2Fe_{12}B$ magnets

Objectives

After completing this project, you will be able to:

- identify the following basic laboratory equipment and demonstrate their proper use: beaker, Erlenmeyer flask, graduated cylinder, pipet, electronic balance.
- properly conduct the following basic laboratory methods: measurement of liquid volume, measurement of sample mass, centrifugation, decantation, gravity filtration.

Introduction

During this procedure you will synthesize magnetite (Fe_3O_4) particles.[1] The balanced equation for formation of the magnetite (Fe_3O_4) product is shown in (1).

$$2\,FeCl_3(aq) + FeCl_2 \cdot 4H_2O(aq) + 8\,NH_3(aq) \longrightarrow Fe_3O_4(s) + 8\,NH_4Cl(aq) \tag{1}$$

As a mineral, magnetite is a black, magnetic rock. The magnetite created here, however, is in the form of nanoscale particles with a diameter of approximately 10 nm. Rather than being a solid, the particles are small enough to be suspended in an aqueous solution. The result is unique: a liquid that has the fluid properties of water and the magnetic properties of magnetite—a magnetic liquid, or *ferrofluid*!

> **NOTE**
>
> **The properties of the ferrofluid are extremely sensitive to the care and precision with which the procedure is followed. Using the wrong amount of a reactant, or adding the ammonia solution too quickly, will ruin the product. The quality of your work during this experiment will be demonstrated in the ferromagnetic properties of your final product.**

Scientific Background

Measure Liquid Volume with a Graduated Cylinder

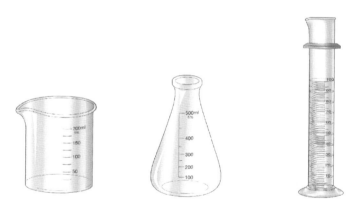

Figure 1-1: Beaker, Erlenmeyer flask, and graduated cylinder.

Variable liquid volumes are commonly measured and delivered using a graduated cylinder, not a beaker or Erlenmeyer flask. The gradation marks on beakers and flasks are approximate, and cannot be used to precisely measure volumes. Pour your liquid into an appropriately-sized graduated cylinder until the bottom of the liquid's meniscus reaches the desired volume. The lowest portion of the curved liquid surface (*meniscus*) is used as the reference point at which the volume measurement is taken. Your eyes should be held at the same level as the meniscus to avoid parallax error. If necessary, a dropper may be used to remove or add small amounts of liquid to reach the desired volume. Before coming to the laboratory, watch the video at http://www.youtube.com/watch?v=D_g0U3vxr18&feature=related on reading burets and pipets.

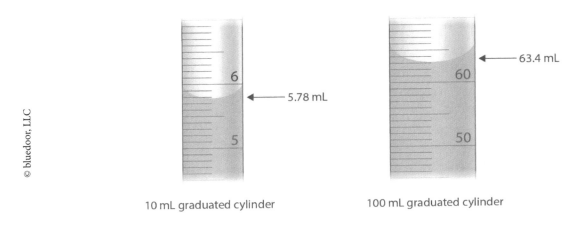

10 mL graduated cylinder   100 mL graduated cylinder

Figure 1-2: Measuring volume using a graduated cylinder.

It is important not to write down too many (or too few) significant figures as the result of a measurement. One of the most common sources of error in experimental data is that due to the uncertainty of estimating fractional parts between scale divisions. Usually one and only one estimated figure is retained and it is regarded as a significant figure. *Figure 1-2* serves to illustrate this point. The 10 mL graduated cylinder is marked in increments of 0.1 mL. The bottom of the meniscus lies over 5.7 mL but under the 5.8 mL mark. The second decimal is estimated and the volume recorded, **with two digits past the decimal**, as 5.78 mL. *What volume of liquid is in the 100 mL graduated cylinder?*

Use of a Stirring Hot Plate

A magnet attached to a motor is under the surface of the stirring hot plate. When the stir dial is turned on, the motor spins the magnet. Stir bars also contain magnets, within a chemically-inert Teflon coating. To stir solutions, place a stir bar inside a container such as a beaker, place it on a stir plate, and turn the stir dial to the lowest setting. Gradually increase the speed of the stirring to avoid splashing the liquid. The spinning magnet inside the stir plate will induce the stir bar to spin within the solution. Be careful not to turn on the heat dial unless you intend to heat your solution, too.

Decant

After standing a few minutes, a precipitate (solid) will often settle to the bottom of a solution, leaving a transparent liquid on top. This liquid is referred to as the supernatant liquid. Remove the supernatant liquid by gently pouring it off or by withdrawing it with a medicine dropper leaving most of the solid behind. Take care not to swirl or jostle the liquid, as this may result in the precipitate being resuspended in the supernatant liquid. This separation procedure is referred to as decantation. Wash the precipitate twice by 1) adding 1 mL of distilled water; 2) stirring with a stirring rod; 3) allowing to settle for a few minutes; and 4) decanting and removing the supernatant liquid.

Gravity Filtration

Using a clamp, mount a funnel in a vertical position on a ring stand. The bottom of the funnel stem should touch the inside of the vessel in which the filtrate is to be collected, about two centimeters below the rim (*Figure 1-3*).

Fold a piece of filter paper along its diameter. Fold again along the radius at right angles to the original fold (*Figure 1-4*). Tear off a small piece of the top corner of one side (*Figure 1-5*). The tear helps the filter paper fit better in the funnel. Place the paper in the funnel with the tear on the outside, against the glass. Wet the paper with distilled water. With your fingers, press the top edge of the paper into the funnel so that no air can pass. Test the filter by filling it with distilled water. The water should soon fill the stem completely, forming a continuous column of liquid that produces a gentle suction promoting filtration, by its hydrostatic pressure. If a continuous column of liquid does not result, air bubbles are present between the funnel and the paper. These bubbles must be dislodged by pressing the paper firmly against the walls of the funnel.

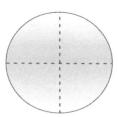

Figure 1-4: Filter paper folding

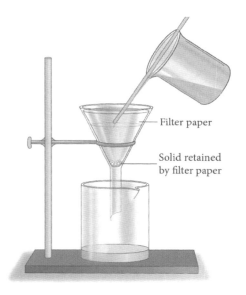

Filter paper

Solid retained by filter paper

© bluedoor, LLC

Figure 1-3: Gravity filtration

Figure 1-5: Location of tear

Filter the suspension by pouring the supernatant liquid down a glass rod held vertically with the lower end resting against the side of the paper in the funnel. Pouring in this way helps to prevent splashing. However, be careful not to punch a hole in the filter paper with the stirring rod. Be patient while filtering. Do not pour too much liquid into the filter paper. The liquid and the precipitate should always be lower than 1/4 inch from the top of the filter paper. Keep the precipitate in the beaker as long as possible, and then pour the suspension down the stirring rod and into the filter. Use water from your distilled water bottle to wash all of the precipitate out of the beaker and into the filter paper. Wash your precipitate at least twice with small amounts of distilled water. Before coming to the laboratory, watch the video at http://www.youtube.com/ watch?v=N0QTRalbH4k&featnre=related on gravity filtration.

Pipet

A pipet is used to deliver a fixed volume of solution. Before using the pipet it should be cleaned and then rinsed with two small portions (~1 mL) of the liquid to be pipetted. Place a pipet pump on the end of your pipet so that the pump is easy to remove. Turn the pipet pump wheel to its lowest setting. Using the wheel, draw liquid into the barrel of the pipet until it is approximately 1 inch above the mark for the volume of liquid required. **CAUTION: Never pipet by mouth; always use a pipet pump.** While filling the pipet, the pipet tip should be kept under the surface of the liquid; otherwise, air will be drawn into the pipet. To deliver liquid from the pipet, remove the pipet pump while instantaneously placing your index finger over the top of the pipet. The flow rate of liquid can then be controlled with your finger. Conversely, liquid can be delivered by keeping the pipet pump in place and turning the wheel, although this is not recommended (heavily used pipet pumps do not form adequate seals). Allow liquid to flow out and into a waste container until the bottom of the meniscus is at the desired volume mark. Drain the rest of the liquid (the desired amount) into your apparatus. Your pipet is made **To Deliver (TD)**; thus, it must be allowed to drain completely on its own without blowing out the last drop. Before coming to the laboratory, watch the video at http://www.youtube .com/watch? v=qorl6rKLmRs on pipetting.

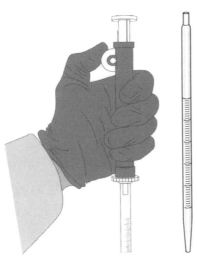

Figure 1-6: Pipet pump & pipet

Centrifuge

Place the test tube containing your sample in one slot of the centrifuge and record the number of that slot (so you know which test tube is yours). Balance the centrifuge by placing a test tube containing an equal volume of water directly opposite your sample. **CAUTION: The centrifuge must be balanced. An unbalanced centrifuge is dangerous because it may wobble and fall from the benchtop.** Turn on the centrifuge for one minute. Allow the centrifuge to come to a stop of its own accord (do not stop it with your hand or any other object), and then remove the test tubes. Remove the supernatant liquid by pouring it off or by withdrawing it with a medicine dropper. Wash the solid twice by 1) adding 1 mL of distilled water; 2) stirring with a stirring rod; and 3) centrifuging and removing the supernatant liquid.

Procedure

Synthesis of a Ferrofluid

1. Work in pairs.

2. Go to the front of the laboratory room and fill your wash bottle with distilled water. Always have a good supply of distilled water in your wash bottle.

3. Use a scoopula to obtain approximately 4 grams of $FeCl_3$ (this amount approximately covers the last half inch of the scoopula) and place into a clean, dry 100 mL beaker.

4. Place a stir bar in the beaker with the $FeCl_3$.

5. Measure 25 mL 2 M HCl solution (from the hood) with a 100 mL graduated cylinder and pour it into the beaker containing the $FeCl_3$.

   - Review **Measure Liquid Volume with a Graduated Cylinder** in the Scientific Background section.

6. Place the beaker on a stir plate and stir slowly to dissolve the $FeCl_3$. Stir for at least 5 minutes.

   - Review **Stirring Hot Plate** in the Scientific Background section.

7. Once the $FeCl_3$ has dissolved, the solution will need to be filtered into a clean 125 mL Erlenmeyer flask to remove any undissolved particles. Label and keep this filtered $FeCl_3$ solution (called filtrate) for Step 12.

   - Review **Gravity Filtration** in the Scientific Background section.

8. Rinse your 100 mL beaker with tap water. Then rinse the beaker twice with distilled water. Invert the beaker to allow most of the distilled water to drain out. This is the standard procedure for reusing laboratory glassware.

   - The inside of the beaker will remain wet, but this is OK for most applications.

   - Do not dry out the inside of the beaker with a towel. Cloth/paper towels add contaminants.

9. Use a scoopula to obtain approximately 4 grams of $FeCl_2 \cdot 4H_2O$ (this amount approximately covers the last half inch of the scoopula) and place into a second clean, dry 100mL beaker.

10. Measure 10 mL 2 M HCl solution with a graduated cylinder and add it to the $FeCl_2 \cdot 4H_2O$. Stir with a glass rod until the solid has fully dissolved.

11. Pipet 1.00 mL of the $FeCl_2 \cdot 4H_2O$ solution into a fresh 100 mL beaker.

    - Review **Pipet** in the Scientific Background section. **Remember: Use a clean pipet and be sure to rinse the pipet with two small portions of the liquid to be measured. Dispose of rinse solutions in the liquid waste container.**

12. Pipet 4.00 mL of $FeCl_3$ solution (the filtrate obtained from Step 7) into the same beaker. Don't forget to first rinse the pipet with the $FeCl_3$ solution before measuring!

13. Swirl the beaker to mix the solutions. Add a dry stir bar to the beaker, place the beaker on a stir plate, and adjust the dial to stir the solution *briskly*, but not so brisk that solution splashes from the beaker.

14. Use a clamp to suspend a buret directly over the beaker on the stir plate. Be sure that the buret stopcock is in the closed position. The tip of the buret should extend below (~2 cm) the upper rim of the beaker.

15. Rinse your 100 mL graduated cylinder with tap water, then rinse twice with distilled water. Invert to allow excess water to drain out. Obtain 25 mL of 10 M NH_3 solution from the hood in the 100 mL cylinder. Add distilled water to the graduated cylinder to dilute the NH_3 solution until the total volume is 50 mL. Use a clean glass stirring rod to stir the solution for 5-10 seconds.

16. Use a minimal amount (2-3 mL) of the NH_3 solution to rinse the buret before pouring half of the diluted NH_3 solution into the buret. Be sure the buret's stopcock is closed before adding the NH_3 solution.

17. Ensure that the stir bar is thoroughly mixing the solution in the beaker. **Carefully** open the stopcock on the buret so that the NH_3 solution is allowed to drain **drop-wise** into the beaker at a rate of no more than one drop per second. **It is extremely important that the NH_3 solution does not drop into the beaker any faster!** If the NH_3 solution is added too fast, then the reaction will fail (i.e., the particle size of your precipitate will be too large and not nanoparticle sized!) and you will need to redo the procedure.

18. Refill (use a funnel) the buret with the second half of the diluted NH_3 solution and continue its drop-wise addition. Wait until all of the NH_3 solution has been added to the beaker. This addition process should take about 20-30 minutes.

19. Turn off the stir plate and allow the solution to settle for at least 5 minutes. During this time, a black precipitate will settle to the bottom of the beaker and a clear solution will remain on top.

20. Gently decant the clear liquid from the black precipitate into another beaker. Review **Decant** in the Scientific Background section.

21. Using forceps, lift the stir bar out of the beaker.

22. Some of the black precipitate should be clinging to the stir bar. Using a stream of distilled water from a wash bottle, gently rinse the black precipitate from the stir bar back into the beaker.

23. Add another 10 mL of distilled water to the precipitate, stir with a glass rod, and allow the precipitate to settle again for 5 minutes. Dry off the stir bar with a paper towel and place it next to the beaker while the solution settles. Since the black particles are magnetic, the attraction to the stir bar's magnet will encourage the precipitate to settle.

24. Again decant the top layer from the black precipitate. Remove as much of the top layer as possible without losing much of the bottom layer. You should end up with not much more than 10 mL of liquid left in the beaker.

25. Obtain two medium test tubes from your teaching assistant. Pour the remaining black sludge from the beaker into one of the test tubes. Do not fill the test tube to the top; leave at least 1 cm of space at the top. Fill the second test tube to the same level with water. Centrifuge the test tubes for one minute. Review **Centrifuge** in the Scientific Background section.

26. After centrifuging, decant the clear liquid from the test tube, leaving behind a thick black goo.

27. Add a few drops of water to the test tube to thin out the black goo, stir with the glass rod, and pour your product into a weigh boat. This product is a ferrofluid, a liquid that exhibits magnetic properties. To best observe the magnetic behavior, you will add a non-polar liquid to "lubricate" the weigh boat.

28. Into the same weigh boat, dispense 3-4 drops of cyclohexane. The black aqueous solution from the test tube will not mix with the cyclohexane. Obtain a magnet from your teaching assistant and bring it up to the underside of the weigh boat. Observe the magnetic properties of the product.

Did you obtain a product?   Yes _____   No _____

Is your product magnetic (i.e., a ferrofluid)? Yes _____   No _____

If not, give an explanation for why it is not magnetic. Where in the procedure did you go wrong?_____

_____

_____

_____

29. Have your teaching assistant observe the magnetic properties of your product and fill in and sign the Experiment 1 Data Report Sheet. Rip off and hand in the data report sheet for grading. Each student is to hand in his/her own data report sheet. However, students working in pairs should include their partner's name on the data report sheet. Dispose of all chemical wastes as indicated by your teaching assistant.

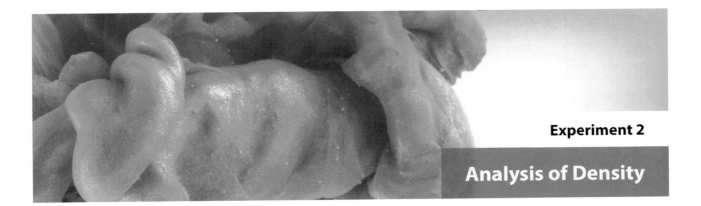

Experiment 2

Analysis of Density

- Chemical splash goggles, gloves, and apron must be worn at all times.

Materials List

- metal samples: copper, brass, aluminum
- polyvinyl chloride (PVC) and Pyrex glass

Objectives

After completing this project, you will be able to:

- calculate the density of a substance from measurements of its mass and volume.

Introduction

Buoyancy and Density

There are a number of methods for determining a material's density. The most widely applicable method takes advantage of buoyancy. According to the principle of buoyancy, any object immersed in water is pushed upward ("buoyed") by a force equal to the weight of the water displaced by the object. Consequently, if a steel ball with a volume of one gallon is suspended by a wire and lowered into a tank of water, the ball will be buoyed by a force equal to the weight of one gallon of water. If you were holding the wire with your hands, you would feel that the ball was less heavy when suspended in the water because of the buoying force. This is also the reason why it is easier to lift a person in a pool of water than in the air.

Since a body of water pushes upward on an immersed object, there must be an equal force pushing down on the water. (Remember equal and opposite forces in physics.) Indeed, if you place a container of water on an electronic balance and lower a massive object into the water, you will find that the apparent mass of the water increases. The mass increase will equal the mass of water displaced by the object. Knowing the mass increase, you could determine the volume of the object also, using the density of water. Knowing the volume of the object and the object's mass, you can calculate the object's density.

For example, one way to estimate the percent fat in a person's body is to measure the person's average density using buoyancy and then use this average density in the Brozek formula.[1] To do so, the person is suspended above a tub of water by a machine that measures their weight. The weight is determined when the body is suspended in air and when it is fully submerged. Consider a person whose mass (by weighing) is 64.05 kg in air and 2.84 kg in water. The mass of water displaced by the body is:

$$\textbf{Mass of displaced water} = 64.05 \text{ kg} - 2.84 \text{ kg} = 61.21 \text{ kg}$$

and the apparent mass of the tub of water increased by 61.21 kg, the mass of displaced water, when the body was submerged. The volume of the displaced water can be found using the density of water [0.9982 g/mL or 0.9982 kg/L at 20 °C]

$$\textbf{Volume of displaced water} = 61.21 \text{ kg} \times \frac{1 \text{ L}}{0.9982 \text{ kg}} = 61.32 \text{ L}$$

The volume of the person's body must have been 61.32 L. To determine the person's average density (d), simply divide their mass (in air) by their volume (remember d = m/V).

$$\textbf{Body density} = \frac{64.05 \text{ kg}}{61.32 \text{ L}} = 1.045 \text{ kg/L} = 1.045 \text{ g/mL}$$

Introduction of this average density into the Brozek formula gives a rough estimate of the person's percent fat.

$$\textbf{Brozek Formula:} \text{ Body Fat \% } = (4.57/d - 4.142) \times 100$$

EXAMPLE:

$$\text{Body Fat \% } = (4.57/1.045 - 4.142) \times 100 = \textbf{\textit{23\% body fat}}$$

Physically fit females and males typically have percent body fat in the ranges 21–24% and 14–17%, respectively. Thus, a percent body fat value of 23% indicates either a physically fit female or a male of average fitness.

Scientific Background

Mass Measurement (Weighing)

Two types of balances will be used in this experiment. The single pan triple-beam balance, shown in *Figure 1-1*, can weigh objects up to several hundred grams with a minimum precision of ±0.01 g. The electronic balance, shown in *Figure 1-2*, can weigh objects up to 310.00 grams with a precision of ±1 mg (±0.001 g).

To minimize errors inherent in the balance, always use the same balance when weighing. Because masses are often obtained by difference, any errors in the balance will be subtracted out when obtaining the difference. Never weigh objects when warm; always allow the object to cool to room temperature before weighing. Warm objects weigh less than cool objects due to convection currents.

---

1 R.W. Johnson. (1996) Fitting Percentage of Body Fat to Simple Body Measurements. J. Stat. Ed. 4 (1) http://www.amstat.org/publications/jse/ v4n1/datasets.johnson.html (accessed Sept. 9, 2009).

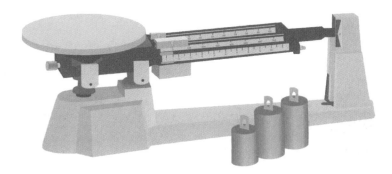

Figure 2-1: Triple-beam balance.

Figure 2-2: Electronic balance.

USING THE TRIPLE-BEAM BALANCE

Be certain that the balance pan, beams, and stand are clean and dry. Place the three sliding weights at the left-hand end of the range. The second (100 g) and third (10 g) slides should catch in the dents at the left which are marked with a zero. Check to see that the balance swings freely, with the center of the pointer swings at the center of the scale marks. If this condition is not attained, have the laboratory teaching assistant adjust the balance.

Place the object to be weighed on the pan and move the 100 g slide first, leaving it in the dent position just short of over-balance. Over-balance occurs when the arm points below the center of the scale indicating that too much weight is on the slides. Next adjust the 10 g slide in the same way. Finally, adjust the small slide until an exact balance is attained. Read the value position of the three slides and add these values together to obtain the object's mass. **NOTE: The 1 g slide arm is marked in increments of 0.1 g; as a result, the second decimal can be estimated.** For example, if the 1 g slide falls about 4/10 of the way between 1.2 g and 1.3 g, the second decimal is estimated and the mass reading reported as 1.24 g.

USING THE ELECTRONIC BALANCE

The electronic balance is an expensive, precision piece of laboratory equipment and must be treated with care. Listed in the table below are the proper procedures to be followed when using the electronic balance. Your laboratory assistant will instruct you on how to use the balance. If difficulty arises in using the electronic balance, ask your laboratory teaching assistant for additional help.

√ BEFORE USING THE BALANCE

- Chemicals or moist objects are not to be placed directly on the balance pan. Clean up any spills on the balance or pan immediately.

- Do not overload the balance. The maximum weight that may be placed on the balance is 310,000 g.

- Always use the same balance when weighing. Any errors inherent in the balance will then be subtracted out.

- Papers and equipment should be cleared from the balance area upon completion of weighing. Paper may be discarded in the wastebaskets in the balance room. There is a container in the hood to hold used weigh boats. All liquids and excess reagents are to be discarded in appropriate waste containers in the laboratory.

- Never place hot objects on the balance pan. Hot objects set up convection currents and give incorrect readings.

- Fingerprints have mass, so do not use bare fingers to handle items to be weighed precisely.

- All pouring, dilutions, etc., of chemicals are to be done at the laboratory bench or on the triple-beam balance and not on the electronic balance or in the balance room.

Before placing a sample on the electronic balance, press the zero button. Automatically, the balance reading will go to 0.000 g. If not, call your laboratory teaching assistant. Place the container into which you will be weighing your chemical on the center pan of the electronic balance. **NOTE: When weighing chemicals, always use a container.** The balance weighs automatically. Read and record the mass of the empty container. At your laboratory desk or on the triple-beam balance, add the proper amount of chemical to the weighed container. Return to the same electronic balance, press the zero button again, and read and record the mass of the container plus chemical. Subtract the mass of the empty container from the mass of container plus chemical to obtain the mass of the chemical. This process is referred to as "*weighing by difference.*" Your teaching assistant will demonstrate the process of weighing by difference before you begin this experiment.

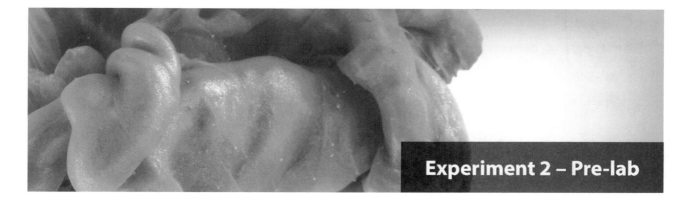

Using calculations similar to those seen in the Introduction, calculate the following:

Consider a beaker of water sitting on the pan of an electronic scale, giving a reading of 113.0 g. A lead weight hanging from a string is suspended in the water and the mass reading on the scale increases to 129.2 g. The lead weight falls from the string, rests on the bottom of the beaker, and the reading becomes 308.8 g. **Note: Be careful of significant figures and include units on all numbers.**

1.   What is the mass of water displaced by the lead weight?

2.   What is the volume of water displaced by the lead weight?

3.   What is the volume of the lead weight?

4.   What is the mass of the lead weight?

5.   What is the density of the lead weight?

Procedure

Density Determinations

1. Work in pairs.

2. Obtain a sample of one of the materials listed in Table 2-1 (see Data Report Sheet).

3. Bring one of the materials, a thin piece of wire, and a 250-mL beaker containing about 100 mL of tap water into the weighing room.

4. Place the beaker on an electronic balance. Tare the reading to zero.

5. Suspending the material from a piece of thin wire, lower it into the water until it is completely submerged, but not touching the bottom of the beaker. You want to submerge as little of the wire as possible. Some have found bending the wire into a small hook aids this effort. The mass reading now corresponds to the mass of water displaced by the material. Record this value in Table 2-1.

6. Allow the material to rest on the bottom of the beaker and release the wire. The mass reading is now the mass of your sample. Record this value in Table 2-1.

7. Return to your lab bench, pour out the water, and dry the beaker, wire, and sample.

8. Repeat Steps 2–6 with each of the other materials listed in Table 2-1.

9. Calculate the volume of each sample using the mass of displaced water and the density of water at 20 °C (0.9982 g/mL). Fill your calculated values into Table 2-1.

10. Calculate the density of each material and fill in your calculated values in Table 2-1.

11. Have your Teaching Assistant verify our completion of this experiment by signing the Data Report Sheet. Rip off and hand in the Data Report Sheet for grading.

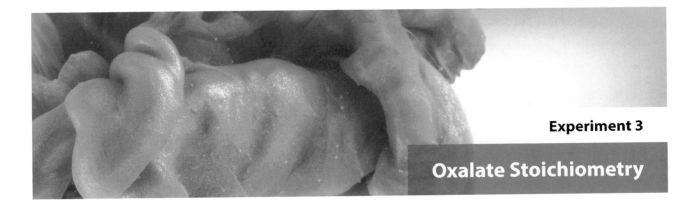

Experiment 3

Oxalate Stoichiometry

Materials List

- 0.888 M oxalic acid, $H_2C_2O_4$
- iron(II)chloride tetrahydrate, $FeCl_2 \cdot 4H_2O$
- nickel(II)nitrate hexahydrate, $Ni(NO_3)_2 \cdot 6H_2O$
- manganese(II)sulfate monohydrate, $MnSO_4 \cdot H_2O$
- acetone, C_3H_6O

Objectives

After completing this project, you will be able to:

- write and balance simple chemical equations.
- convert between grams, moles, volume, and molar mass.
- calculate amount of reactant or product given amount of other reactants or products using the balanced chemical equation.
- identify the limiting reagent in a reaction.
- calculate the theoretical yield of a reaction and amount of unused excess reagent when given the amounts of reactants.
- convert between actual yield, percent yield, and theoretical yield.

Introduction

Kidney stones are a common medical condition for not just humans, but also dogs, cats, and even iguanas.[1] Chemically, most kidney stones are calcium oxalate formed by the precipitation of calcium ions with oxalate ions ($C_2O_4^{2-}$) in the urine.[2] Oxalates block the absorption of important nutrients, such as calcium and iron, resulting in increased metal ion concentrations, and subsequent oxalate precipitation and kidney stone formation.[3] Surprisingly, increased consumption of calcium in the diet is not correlated with increased occurrence of kidney stones.[2] However, eating high content oxalic acid foods, such as spinach, nuts, rhubarb, and sesame seeds, does lead to more kidney stones.[4] According to Guinness World Records, the heaviest kidney stone reported weighed 620 g (21.87 oz) and had to be surgically removed from the kidney of a man in Pakistan in 2008.[5] Many kidney stones are passed without incident. However, once stones reach 2–3 mm in diameter a person will experience significant pain.

Are there any other reasons oxalates are important? **Yes!** From kidney stones and metal oxide nanoparticle formation to oxalate's role in joint inflammation and autism and to their use as pigments and as evidence of life on Mars, the importance of oxalates is evident!

Oxalates in Context

Metal Oxalate	Effect or Use
Calcium Oxalate	Kidney stones in humans and animals[1-4]
Transition Metal Oxalates	As precursors to metal oxide nanoparticles[6,7,8], applications in catalysis[9] and semi-conductors[10]
Iron(II)oxalate	Used as yellow pigment: paints, glass, and plastic
Naturally Occurring Metal Oxalates e.g., FeC_2O_4 (humboldtine)	Product of fungi/lichen growth: presence used as evidence for life on other planets[11]
Metal Oxalate Crystals	Formation in bones/joints: associated with inflammation, anemia,[12] immunosuppression
Low Oxalate Diet	As treatment for autism: preliminary research indicates that autistic children have high amounts of oxalates in urine[13,14]

Many metal ions, except for Group 1A, the alkali metals, form an oxalate precipitate at low oxalic acid concentrations. In human urine, the most abundant precipitating metal ion is calcium, which leads to the common form of kidney stones. This experiment will examine the precipitate formed by oxalic acid with other metals, such as iron, nickel, and manganese.

---

1 Robinson, M.R.; Norris, R.D., Sur, R.L., Premingeret, G.M. J. Urol. 2008, 179, 46–52.

2 Curhan, G.C. et al. N. Eng. J. Med. 1993, 328, 833–838.

3 Walker, N. J. Chem. Educ. 1988, 65, 533.

4 Massey, L.K.; Roman-Smith H.;Sutton, R.A. J. Am. Diet Assoc. 1993, 93, 901–906.

5 Guiness World Records. http://www.guinnessworldrecords.com/records/human_body/ medcal_marvels/heaviest_kidney_stone.aspx (accessed March 16, 2010).

Scientific Background

Vacuum Filtration

Vacuum filtration is much faster and more efficient than gravity filtration. To perform vacuum filtration, first attach the vacuum flask to a ring stand using a clamp. Once the entire apparatus is set up, it will be top-heavy and prone to falling over. Place a Büchner funnel in the mouth of the clamped vacuum flask and attach the sidearm of the vacuum flask to a vacuum line using thick rubber tubing (see Figure 3-1). Place a round piece of filter paper in the funnel and dampen it so that it sticks to the plate of the funnel and covers the holes. Turn on the vacuum line, and water and air will be drawn through the filter paper into the flask. At this point, the procedure closely follows the gravity filtration procedure you followed when using filter paper in a conical funnel.

Figure 3-1: Büchner funnel atop a vacuum flask. Be sure to clamp!

Filter the suspension by pouring the supernatant liquid down a glass rod held vertically with the lower end resting against the center of the filter paper. Pouring in this way helps to prevent splashing. However, be careful not to punch a hole in the filter paper with the stirring rod. Be patient while filtering. Do not pour too much liquid into the filter paper. The liquid and the precipitate should always be lower than 1/2 of the way to the top rim of the funnel. Keep the precipitate in the beaker as long as possible, and then pour the suspension down the stirring rod and into the filter. To remove impurities, be sure to wash the precipitate several times with solvent.

Prelab: Preparatory Stoichiometry

Your laboratory procedure will be different from your classmates', depending on your laboratory desk number. Complete the prelab assignment (associated with your laboratory desk number) before coming to the laboratory for this experiment. For instance, if your laboratory desk is 20, then you will complete pages 21 and 22 (prelab for desk 20). If desk 13, then you will complete pages 19 and 20 (prelab for desk 13).

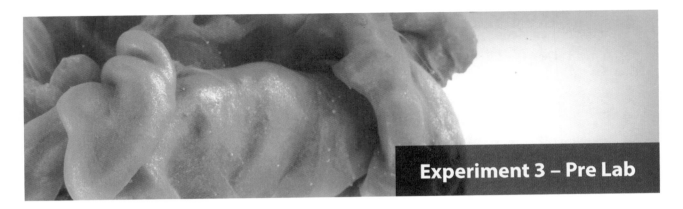

For desk numbers 1, 4, 7, 10, 13, 16, 19, and 22

Answer the following questions. Show all work and calculations to support your answers. Include the correct units and the proper number of significant figures on numerical answers. Circle your final answers.

1. For the metal salt indicated in the procedure, you should use $FeCl_2 \cdot 4H_2O$. Calculate the molar mass of $FeCl_2 \cdot 4H_2O$.

2. Your oxalate synthesis product will be $FeC_2O_4 \cdot 2H_2O$. Calculate the molar mass of $FeC_2O_4 \cdot 2H_2O$.

3. Write a balanced molecular equation that shows your metal salt, $FeCl_2 \cdot 4H_2O$, reacting with oxalic acid ($H_2C_2O_4$) to form $FeC_2O_4 \cdot 2H_2O$. What will be the other product(s) of the reaction?

4. Pyrolysis of $FeC_2O_4 \cdot 2H_2O$ will follow one of the following molecular equations. Balance each molecular equation.

    a. $FeC_2O_4 \cdot 2H_2O(s)$ + $O_2(g)$ → $FeO(s)$ + $H_2O(g)$ + $CO_2(g)$

    b. $FeC_2O_4 \cdot 2H_2O(s)$ + $O_2(g)$ → $Fe_2O_3(s)$ + $H_2O(g)$ + $CO_2(g)$

    c. $FeC_2O_4 \cdot 2H_2O(s)$ → $FeCO_3(s)$ + $H_2O(g)$ + $CO(g)$

5. For each of the possible pyrolysis reactions, calculate the theoretical yield (in grams) of the solid product, assuming that you use 1.0 g $FeC_2O_4 \cdot 2H_2O$ and that oxygen is the excess reactant. You will need to write in coefficients from Question 4 to balance the molecular equations.

    a. $FeC_2O_4 \cdot 2H_2O(s)$ + $O_2(g)$ → $FeO(s)$ + $H_2O(g)$ + $CO_2(g)$
             1.0 g   ? g

    b. $FeC_2O_4 \cdot 2\,H_2O(s)$ + $O_2(g)$ → $Fe_2O_3(s)$ + $H_2O(g)$ + $CO_2(g)$
             1.0 g   ? g

    c. $FeC_2O_4 \cdot 2H_2O(s)$ → $FeCO_3(s)$ + $H_2O(g)$ + $CO(g)$
             1.0 g   ? g

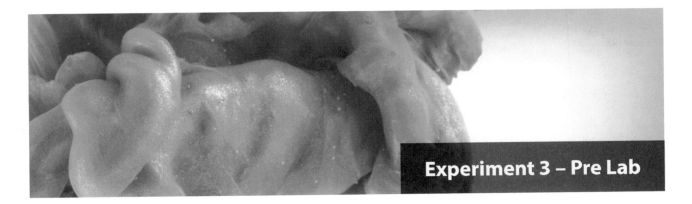

For desk numbers 2, 5, 8, 11, 14, 17, 20, and 23

Answer the following questions. Show all work and calculations to support your answers. Include the correct units and the proper number of significant figures on numerical answers. Circle your final answers.

1. For the metal salt indicated in the procedure, you should use $Ni(NO_3)_2 \cdot 6H_2O$. Calculate the molar mass of $Ni(NO_3)_2 \cdot 6H_2O$.

2. Your oxalate synthesis product will be $NiC_2O_4 \cdot 2H_2O$. Calculate the molar mass of $NiC_2O_4 \cdot 2H_2O$.

3. Write a balanced molecular equation that shows your metal salt, $Ni(NO_3)_2 \cdot 6H_2O$, reacting with oxalic acid $(H_2C_2O_4)$ to form $NiC_2O_4 \cdot 2H_2O$. What will be the other product(s) of the reaction?

4. Pyrolysis of $NiC_2O_4 \cdot 2H_2O$ will follow one of the following molecular equations. Balance each molecular equation.

    a. $NiC_2O_4 \cdot 2H_2O(s)$ + $O_2(g)$ $\rightarrow$ $NiO(s)$ + $H_2O(g)$ + $CO_2(g)$

    b. $NiC_2O_4 \cdot 2H_2O(s)$ + $O_2(g)$ $\rightarrow$ $Ni_2O_3(s)$ + $H_2O(g)$ + $CO_2(g)$

    c. $NiC_2O_4 \cdot 2H_2O(s)$ $\rightarrow$ $NiCO_3(s)$ + $H_2O(g)$ + $CO(g)$

5. For each of the possible pyrolysis reactions, calculate the theoretical yield (in grams) of the solid product, assuming that you use 1.0 g $NiC_2O_4 \cdot 2H_2O$ and that oxygen is the excess reactant. You will need to write in coefficients from Question 4 to balance the molecular equations.

    a. $NiC_2O_4 \cdot 2H_2O(s)$ + $O_2(g)$ $\rightarrow$ $NiO(s)$ + $H_2O(g)$ + $CO_2(g)$
             1.0 g   ? g

    b. $NiC_2O_4 \cdot 2H_2O(s)$ + $O_2(g)$ $\rightarrow$ $Ni_2O_3(s)$ + $H_2O(g)$ + $CO_2(g)$
             1.0 g   ? g

    c. $NiC_2O_4 \cdot 2H_2O(s)$ $\rightarrow$ $NiCO_3(s)$ + $H_2O(g)$ + $CO(g)$
             1.0 g   ? g

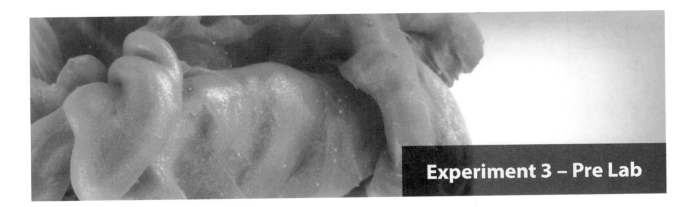

For desk numbers 3, 6, 9, 12, 15, 18, 21, and 24

Answer the following questions. Show all work and calculations to support your answers. Include the correct units and the proper number of significant figures on numerical answers. Circle your final answers.

1. For the metal salt indicated in the procedure, you should use $MnSO_4 \cdot H_2O$. Calculate the molar mass of $MnSO_4 \cdot H_2O$.

2. Your oxalate synthesis product will be $MnC_2O_4 \cdot 3H_2O$. Calculate the molar mass of $MnC_2O_4 \cdot 3H_2O$.

3. Write a balanced molecular equation that shows your metal salt, $MnSO_4 \cdot H_2O$, reacting with oxalic acid ($H_2C_2O_4$) and water to form $MnC_2O_4 \cdot 3H_2O$. What will be the other product(s) of the reaction?

4. Pyrolysis of $MnC_2O_4 \cdot 3H_2O$ will follow one of the following molecular equations. Balance each molecular equation.

   a. $MnC_2O_4 \cdot 3H_2O(s)$ + $O_2(g)$ → $MnO(s)$ + $H_2O(g)$ + $CO_2(g)$

   b. $MnC_2O_4 \cdot 3H_2O(s)$ + $O_2(g)$ → $Mn_3O_4(s)$ + $H_2O(g)$ + $CO_2(g)$

   c. $MnC_2O_4 \cdot 3H_2O(s)$ → $MnCO_3(s)$ + $H_2O(g)$ + $CO(g)$

5. For each of the possible pyrolysis reactions, calculate the theoretical yield (in grams) of the solid product, assuming that you use 1.0 g $MnC_2O_4 \cdot 3 H_2O$ and that oxygen is the excess reactant. You will need to write in coefficients from Question 4 to balance the molecular equations.

   a. $MnC_2O_4 \cdot 3H_2O(s)$ + $O_2(g)$ → $MnO(s)$ + $H_2O(g)$ + $CO_2(g)$
           1.0 g   ? g

   b. $MnC_2O_4 \cdot 3H_2O(s)$ + $O_2(g)$ → $Mn_3O_4(s)$ + $H_2O(g)$ + $CO_2(g)$
           1.0 g   ? g

   c. $MnC_2O_4 \cdot 3H_2O(s)$ → $MnCO_3(s)$ + $H_2O(g)$ + $CO(g)$
           1.0 g   ? g

Procedure

Part I: Synthesis of a Metal Oxalate

Do not work in pairs. All students are to work individually. You will be synthesizing a metal oxalate from a metal salt and oxalic acid via the reaction outlined in Question #3 of your prelab.

1. Weigh between 3.9 g and 4.1 g of your hydrated metal salt (as determined by your desk number (see prelab) into a small beaker using the method of weighing by difference (see below). Record the metal salt's exact mass in Table 3-1. Add 20 mL distilled water and stir to dissolve.

    - To minimize errors inherent in the balance, always use the same balance when weighing.

    - *Weighing by difference*: On an electronic balance, obtain the mass of a clean, dry, empty, beaker. Record your mass measurement using all numbers in the display (this will be either two or three decimal places, depending on the particular balance used). Take this beaker to the triple-beam balance and add 3.9 to 4.1 g of metal salt. Return to the same electronic balance and obtain the mass of the beaker plus chemical (to three places after the decimal!). Record this mass and subtract to obtain the mass of metal salt.

        Mass of Beaker + Metal Salt   = _____

        Mass of Empty Beaker   = _____

        Mass of Hydrated Metal Salt   = _____

2. Use a graduated cylinder to precisely measure 50.0 mL of oxalic acid solution. Place the oxalic acid solution in a separate beaker. The solution contains 4.0 g oxalic acid ($H_2C_2O_4$) per 50.0 mL of solution.

3. Once the metal salt is completely dissolved, slowly pour the metal salt solution into the oxalic acid solution. Stir to mix and allow the solution to sit for 10 minutes while a precipitate forms.

4. Prepare a Büchner funnel (as explained in the Scientific Background) while the precipitate is forming. Before placing the filter paper in the Büchner funnel, be sure to weigh and record the mass of your filter paper in Table 3-1.

5. After the waiting period, begin suction through the filter paper in the funnel and slowly pour your solution onto the center of the filter paper. It is important to try to keep the majority of the precipitate in the center of the paper rather than sticking to the funnel walls. The precipitate should be retained on the filter paper as the aqueous solution is drawn into the flask below.

6. Once the entire solution has been emptied into the funnel, add 20 mL of distilled water to the beaker, swirl the beaker to suspend any remaining precipitate, and also pour this into the funnel. You must transfer all of the precipitate from the beaker. Repeat this step as often as needed to get all the precipitate into the funnel.

7. The precipitate will still be wet with water, so you will need to wash the precipitate with acetone. You can do this while the vacuum is still running.

8. Obtain a red-capped acetone wash bottle from under the hood. Gently squirt ~5 mL of acetone over the precipitate in the funnel. Use the pressure from the wash bottle to focus the acetone

stream on the sides of the funnel, thus forcing more of the solid back toward the center of the paper. DO NOT add the acetone too quickly or you risk displacing the filter paper and losing sample. Using a glass rod, carefully stir the solid so that all of it is in contact with the acetone. Make sure any solid sticking to the stir rod ends up back on the filter paper (use the acetone wash bottle). During this time, any water on the precipitate particles will dissolve in the acetone and facilitate the drying of your sample.

 CAUTION: Acetone is flammable! Keep this liquid away from open flames.

9. Repeat Step 8 with two additional washes of ~5 mL of acetone.

    - **Limit your use of acetone to the minimum amount needed to wash your precipitate.**

    - **Use no more than ~20 mL total for washing your precipitate.**

10. Keep the vacuum on to draw air through the filter paper. The acetone will evaporate from the solid. Keep the vacuum on until the solid is dry. You can push around the precipitate with a glass rod to test for dryness. Once the solid is completely dry, turn off the vacuum.

    - **Be patient!** The drier your solid product, the more accurate your results.

    - This solid product must be **completely dry** before beginning Part II of the procedure.

11. Obtain a weigh dish, find its mass on an electronic balance, and record its mass in Table 3-1. Transfer the dry solid to the weigh dish and determine the mass of the dish plus contents. It may be easier to transfer the entire filter paper and just subtract out the paper's weight. Subtract to obtain the actual yield of hydrated metal oxalate precipitate in Table 3-1.

    mass of weigh dish + contents   =   _____

    mass of empty weigh dish   =   _____

    mass of filter paper   =   _____

    actual yield of hydrated metal oxalate precipitate =   _____

    color of hydrated metal oxalate   =   _____

12. Using the data collected (i.e., masses of hydrated metal salt and oxalic acid reacted and actual yield of hydrated metal oxalate precipitate) and the balanced reaction for the formation of the metal oxalate product (see prelab Question #3), determine a) the identity of the limiting reactant; b) theoretical yield of the hydrated metal oxalate, and; c) the percent yield of the hydrated metal oxalate product. Complete Table 3-1.

    Calculations: Show your calculations below. Watch your units and report all answers with the correct number of significant figures.

Procedure

Part II: Pyrolysis of a Metal Oxalate

What is pyrolysis?

Pyrolysis is the process of causing a chemical reaction to occur by heating a substance. If air is present, then pyrolysis may also involve reactions with O_2 or N_2.

You will be pyrolyzing the metal oxalate you synthesized in Part I. You will use stoichiometric considerations to determine which pyrolysis reaction (of those given in prelab Question #4) your metal oxalate undergoes.

1. Using the process of weighing by difference (see Procedure, Part 1 and Step 1), precisely measure between 0.990 g and 1.010 g of your dry, hydrated metal oxalate into an *aluminum* dish. Record precise masses in Table 3-2.

   - To enhance heat transfer, spread out the solid over the bottom of the dish.

   - It is important to use between 0.990 g and 1.010 g because your prelab calculations were based upon pyrolysis of 1.0 g of hydrated metal oxalate.

   - Pouring of chemicals should be done at the laboratory bench or on the triple-beam balance and not on the electronic balance or in the balance room.

   - Masses obtained using the electronic balance should be given with three decimal places.

mass of alum. dish + hydrated metal oxalate	=	_____
mass of empty aluminum dish	=	_____
mass of hydrated metal oxalate before pyrolysis	=	_____

2. Turn the dial on a hot plate to one-half of the maximum setting. Place the aluminum dish on the hot plate. The hydrated metal oxalate will undergo dehydration (loss of water) followed by a pyrolysis reaction once it reaches a certain temperature.

3. Wait until the metal oxalate has been heated at least 10 minutes. As the oxalate heats, carefully push it around with a clean glass rod to promote drying. Remove the aluminum dish from the hot plate using a pair of metal tongs and place it on the laboratory bench to cool to room temperature. The aluminum dish should cool quickly but the precipitate may take longer.

 CAUTION: The aluminum dish will be VERY hot…make sure to use the tongs!

   - **Be patient!** The cooler the precipitate, the better your results.

   - Never weigh hot objects. Hot objects weigh less than cool objects due to convection currents.

4. Weigh the cooled aluminum dish plus contents and record its mass.

    After first heating: mass of aluminum dish + contents   =   _____

5. Place the aluminum dish back on the hot plate, turn the heat to ~ 400 °C, and heat for another 10 minutes, cool to room temperature, and reweigh. If the mass of the dish plus contents has not changed by more than 10 mg (0.010 g), then record the final mass of the dish and product in Table 3-2. If the mass of the dish plus contents has changed by more than 10 mg (decreased or increased), then increase the heat (go to a higher temperature, perhaps 450 °C) and heat again for another 10 minutes, cool to room temperature, and reweigh. Repeat this process until the mass remains constant.

    - This process of heating, cooling, and reweighing the substance until constant mass is achieved is referred to as "bringing to constant mass."

    - Your pyrolysis product should be homogeneous in terms of color. If your pyrolysis product has chunks of yellow intermixed with chunks of black, then pyrolysis is not complete.

    - If you are working with the nickel oxalate, do NOT stop the pyrolysis at the intermediate yellow colored substance but rather continue on until you obtain a black substance.

    After second heating: Mass of aluminum dish + contents = _____

    After third heating: Mass of aluminum dish + contents = _____(if needed)

    After fourth heating: Mass of aluminum dish + contents = _____(if needed)

6. Complete Table 3-2. The pyrolysis reaction occurs with near 100% yield, so the actual yield of the pyrolysis reaction should be very close to the theoretical yield you calculated for the correct reaction equation (as calculated in Question #5 of the prelab).

    After pyrolysis:

Mass (final) of dish + pyrolysis product	=	_____
Mass of empty aluminum dish	=	_____
Mass (actual) of pyrolysis product	=	_____
Color of pyrolysis product	=	_____

7. Double-check all of your calculations and significant figures. Include units on all of your numbers. Have your Teaching Assistant verify by signing your completion of this experiment. Rip off and hand in the Data Report Sheet for grading. Dispose of all chemical wastes as indicated by your Teaching Assistant.

    Which of three possible pyrolysis reactions (reaction A, B, or C) actually occurred? _____

    What is the chemical formula of the pyrolysis product from the chosen reaction? _____

Calculations: Show your calculations below. Watch your units and report all answers with the correct number of significant figures.

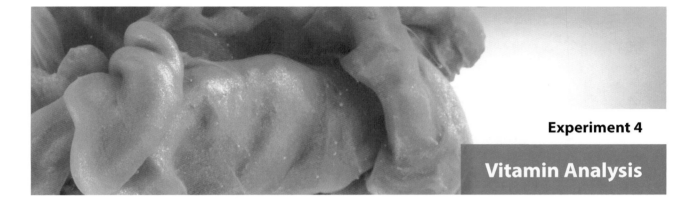

Experiment 4

Vitamin Analysis

- Chemical splash goggles, gloves, and apron must be worn at all times.

- Tie back long hair and loose sleeves.

- Acid solutions are corrosive. Immediately wash all spills with excess water and inform the Teaching Assistant.

- Hot plates are being used to heat acidic solutions. Take extra caution in handling the hot glassware as hot acid is extremely dangerous.

- Be careful of hot objects. Immediately place any burns under cold water and inform the Teaching Assistant.

- Carry out reactions and heating under the student hood to minimize exposure to noxious fumes. Make sure the student hood is firmly seated against the rubber gasket.

- Do not taste the vitamins. Food items brought into a chemistry laboratory are no longer safe to eat.

Materials List

- ammonium peroxodisulfate, $(NH_4)_2S_2O_8$
- 6 M hydrochloric acid, HCl

- ammonium thiocyanate, NH_4SCN
- iron(III)nitrate nonahydrate $Fe(NO_3)_3 \cdot 9H_2O$, acidified

Objectives

After completing this project, you will be able to:

- convert between molarity, volume of solution, and amount of solute.

- collect and interpret gravimetric, volumetric, and spectroscopic chemical data to formulate conclusions.

- properly conduct the following basic laboratory techniques: gravimetric analysis and absorbance spectroscopy.

- prepare a solution in the following ways: using a solid, using a dilution of an existing solution, and implementing a serial dilution.

Introduction

The absorbance of light by a colored solution is directly proportional to the concentration of dissolved substance within the solution. Solution concentration is mostly measured in units of molarity (M), which denotes *moles of solute dissolved per liter of solution (mol/L)*. Most molecules absorb light energy within their bonds. A wide range of energies can be absorbed, which corresponds to different colors. Chemists measure absorbance with instruments called colorimeters or spectrophotometers, which calculate how much of a given initial light sample is absorbed by the sample. For example, consider the following scenario (Figure 4-1):

A chemist is provided with a blue solution of copper(II)sulfate, $CuSO_4$, dissolved in water; call this the unknown solution (US). The chemist takes 10 mL of the unknown solution and adds 90 mL of water to make 100 mL of a new solution, Dilution #1. Dilution #1 is the unknown solution diluted by 10:100, or 1:10. Therefore, the concentration of $CuSO_4$ in Dilution #1 is 1/10 that of the unknown solution. Dilution #1 is similarly diluted by 10:100 to make Dilution #2. This process is termed a **serial dilution** because the solution is sequentially diluted using a constant dilution factor for each step. After the serial dilution is complete, the chemist determines that the absorbance of red light by Dilution #2 is 0.15. The $CuSO_4$ appears blue because it absorbs red light but does not absorb blue light (the complementary color to red).

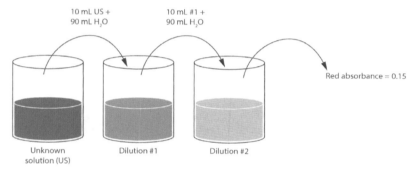

10 mL US +
90 mL H_2O

10 mL #1 +
90 mL H_2O

Red absorbance = 0.15

Unknown
solution (US)

Dilution #1

Dilution #2

Figure 4-1: Serial Dilution

The chemist must now determine the concentration of $CuSO_4$ in the unknown solution by comparing the absorbance of Dilution #2 to the absorbance of a known concentration of $CuSO_4$ (i.e., a standard solution). Therefore, the chemist makes a 0.050 M standard solution of $CuSO_4$ (0.050 mol $CuSO_4$/1 L soln), and finds that its red light absorbance value is 0.76. By using the fact that absorbance (A) and concentration (C) are proportional (i.e., A ∝ C and A = εbC), the chemist is able to construct a proportionality constant using the known values of the standard solution.

$$\frac{\text{concentration of } CuSO_4 \text{ in KNOWN solution}}{\text{absorbance of } CuSO_4 \text{ in KNOWN solution}} = \frac{0.050 \text{ M}}{0.76}$$

This proportionality constant can be used to calculate the concentration of $CuSO_4$ in an unknown solution if the absorbance of that solution is known.

$$\frac{0.050 \text{ M}}{0.76} \times \text{absorbance } CuSO_4 \text{ in unknown soln.} = \text{concentration of } CuSO_4 \text{ in an unknown soln.}$$

Using the above equation and the absorbance value of 0.15 for Dilution #2, you can determine that the concentration of $CuSO_4$ in Dilution #2 is 0.0099 M.

$$\frac{0.050 \text{ M}}{0.76} \times 0.15 = 0.0098684 \text{ mol CuSO}_4/\text{L soln} = 0.0099 \text{ M CuSO}_4$$

Since Dilution #1 was 10x more concentrated than Dilution #2 (remember: 10 mL of Dilution #1 was diluted to 100 mL to make Dilution #2), the concentration of $CuSO_4$ in Dilution #1 was 0.099 M. One can use the following dilution relationship to calculate the concentration of Dilution #1. In this equation, M_1 and M_2 are solution concentrations in terms of molarity and V_1 and V_2 are solution volumes.

$$M_1 \times V_1 = M_2 \times V_2$$

$$M_1 \times 10 \text{ mL} = 0.0099 \text{ M} \times 100 \text{ mL}$$

$$M_1 = \frac{0.0099 \text{ M} \times 100 \text{mL}}{10 \text{ mL}} = 0.099 \text{ M}$$

Since the original unknown solution was 10x more concentrated than Dilution #1 (remember: 10 mL of the unknown solution was diluted to 100 mL to make Dilution #1), the concentration of $CuSO_4$ in the original unknown solution was 0.99 M.

$$M_{US} \times V_{US} = M_1 \times V_1$$

$$M_{US} \times 10 \text{ mL} = 0.0099 \text{ M} \times 100 \text{ mL}$$

$$M_1 = \frac{0.099 \text{ M} \times 100 \text{mL}}{10 \text{ mL}} = 0.99 \text{ M}$$

Scientific Background

Serial dilution is one of the most widely practiced laboratory techniques and is particularly fundamental to the analytical chemistry discipline. The vast majority of forensic laboratories implement serial dilution protocols when working with highly concentrated samples such as blood or urine. In fact, many automated serial dilution systems have been constructed on microchips.[1,2] Microchips (see Figure 4-2) allow scientists the flexibility to use minute amounts of a sample that is precious or in short supply. In addition, microchips are relatively inexpensive to manufacture and are therefore disposable.

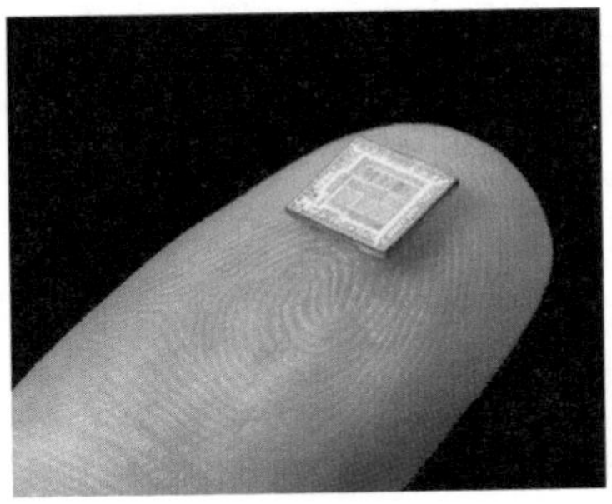

© bluedoor, LLC

Figure 4-2: Picture of a Microchip

1 Pagel, B.M. et al. Anal. Chem. 2006 November 1; 78(21):7522–7527.
2 Koehler, J. et al. ASSAY and Drug Development Technologies, 2002 November 1(1):91–96.

The serial dilution technique is so essential to science that it has found its way into other fields such as molecular biology, cell biology, drug development, and genetic engineering, to name a few. Serial dilutions made culturing and counting bacteria cells more efficient, especially once automated systems were developed. Microchip serial dilution systems are now used to construct dose-response assays, which are essential to the development of new drug candidates. Dose-response assays measure either the therapeutic or toxic effect of varying drug doses on biological organisms.

Iron is essential to humans and its absence or deficiency can lead to serious health problems and possible death. Iron is found in the molecule hemoglobin, which transports oxygen around the body via the blood. Oxygen molecules actually bind to iron atoms within hemoglobin and are released upon reaching oxygen-deficient cells or tissues. Iron deficiency is called anemia and is a common medical issue still being researched today.[3] In fact, intravenous iron therapy is one of the most prevalent treatments for inflammatory bowel disease.[4]

---

3   Gomollón F., Gisbert J.P. World J Gastroenterol. 2009 Oct 7;15(37);4659–65.
4   Muñoz M., Gómez-Ramírez S., García-Erce J.A. World J Gastroenterol. 2009 Oct7;15(37);4666–74.

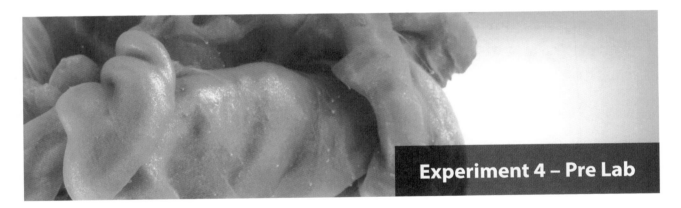

You have been given a jar of red fruit punch and been asked to determine the concentration of the red dye in the fruit punch. It is known that a 0.00010 M standard solution of this red dye absorbs green light (the complementary color) with an absorbance value of 0.77.

You decide to measure the absorbance of the fruit punch, but your colorimeter only works properly for absorbance values between 0.1 and 0.9 (which is common). As a result, the absorbance value for your fruit punch must be between 0.1 and 0.9 or your data will be worthless because you have either (i) exceeded the detection limit of your colorimeter or (ii) reached a point where concentration and absorbance are no longer directly proportional. Your fruit punch is dark red in color and you deduce that your fruit punch is too concentrated and will have a green light absorbance much greater than 0.9 (i.e., out of range of your colorimeter). Therefore, you will have to do a serial dilution. You take 5.0 mL of the fruit punch and dilute it **to** 100.0 mL using distilled water. You call this new solution Dilution #1. You then take 5.0 mL of Dilution #1 and dilute it **to** 100.0 mL using distilled water; you call this Dilution #2. The solution in Dilution #2 absorbs green light with an absorbance value of 0.21.

1. Using the procedure you read about in the introduction section (pages 30–31), calculate the concentration of red dye in the Dilution #2 solution.

2. Calculate the concentration of red dye in the Dilution #1 solution.

3. Calculate the concentration of red dye in the original sample of fruit punch.

Procedure

Quantitative Analysis of Iron

A. SAMPLE PREPARATION

Work in pairs on all parts of this experiment. It can be lengthy so be efficient in your use of time.

1. Obtain your vitamin tablet sample from your Teaching Assistant. Record your sample number (see top of bottle) on the Data Report Sheet. The vitamin contains iron in the form of small particles of iron metal or as an ionic iron salt. You will determine the exact mass of iron in the tablet.

    - This process is extremely sensitive to your care and cleanliness during the procedure.
    - Glassware must be rinsed carefully, and procedures followed precisely.
    - Volume measurements must be made carefully, being sure not to overshoot or undershoot the level markings on the volumetric flask or volumetric pipet.
    - Contamination of your solutions will throw off your results.

2. During waiting times in the sample preparation, go on to later parts of the procedure to make efficient use of your time in laboratory.

3. Obtain a weigh dish and use the electronic balance to find the mass of the empty weigh dish. Record this mass below (in Step 4).

> **NOTE**
>
> **Do not pour chemicals, prepare chemicals, or react chemicals in the balance room or over the electronic balances! All pouring, preparation, and reaction of chemicals is to be carried out at your laboratory desk and under your student hood!**

4. If your vitamin is in capsule form, remove the coating and quantitatively transfer the powder to the weigh dish. If your vitamin is in tablet form, obtain a clean, dry mortar and pestle and use the mortar and pestle to pulverize your tablet. Quantitatively transfer the powdered tablet to the weigh dish. On the electronic balance, obtain the mass of the weigh dish and sample and by subtraction the mass of the powdered tablet. Record the mass of the powdered tablet on the Data Report Sheet.

    - Be sure to use the same electronic balance for all mass readings. In this way, errors inherent in the balance will be subtracted out.
    - Clean and dry the mortar and pestle before giving it to another student to use.

    Mass of weigh dish + powdered tablet   =   _____

    Mass of empty weigh dish   =   _____

    Mass of powdered tablet   =   _____

5. Quantitatively transfer the powdered tablet to a 125-mL Erlenmeyer flask. Add 25 mL of 6 M HCl. Put your magnetic stir bar into the flask and turn on the stirring function. Gently heat the solution on a hot plate while stirring for 15 minutes to dissolve the tablet and to convert any iron metal to dissolved Fe^{3+} ions.

CAUTION: 6 M HCl is highly corrosive. Use gloves, goggles, and aprons.

- Additionally, heat the flask inside your student hood as the fumes from the acid are also corrosive!

6. Once your tablet is dissolved in the acid, turn off and unplug the hot plate. Add 0.2 g ammonium peroxodisulfate, $(NH_4)_2S_2O_8$, to the solution and mix. This compound will oxidize any components of the tablet that might interfere with the analysis of the iron ions.

7. Let the solution cool to near room temperature. Make sure the solution has cooled off before you try and move it from the hot plate. Proceed to Step 8 and on to Part B, Instrument Setup while the acid solution continues to cool.

8. In a separate beaker, weigh out 3.0 g of ammonium thiocyanate, NH_4SCN. Add 10 mL distilled water to the beaker and stir to dissolve. If this solution turns red before you add any iron(III), then your glassware is contaminated and you will need to prepare this solution again. The NH_4SCN solution, when mixed with dissolved iron(III) ions, will produce a dark red ion $[Fe(SCN)]^{2+}$. The absorbance of blue light by this ion is directly proportional to its concentration in the solution, which in turn is directly proportional to the concentration of iron in the solution.

B. INSTRUMENT SETUP

1. Turn on the SPARK unit.

2. Connect the cord from the colorimeter box to the top of the SPARK unit. The screen should change to show that the colorimeter has been connected. Scroll down to find the absorbance readout for the absorbance of blue light.

3. Fill one colorimeter sample vial with distilled water, cap the vial, wipe off the sides of the vial with a Kimwipe, and place the vial in the colorimeter sample compartment (see Figure 4-3). Close the lid and press the green button that is located on the black sensor unit. The light on the button should go on and the screen should read zero for the absorbance of blue light (or very close to zero). This step ensures that the colorimeter is calibrated.

- NOTE: Once you have pressed the green button for your water sample, DO NOT push it again for the remainder of the experiment.

- Use this same colorimeter vial for all measurements. In this way, absorbance due to the vial itself is canceled out.

4. Remove the water sample and empty the vial.

C. PREPARATION AND ANALYSIS OF THE STANDARD SOLUTION

1. Obtain approximately 12 mL of the iron(III) stock solution, $Fe(NO_3)_3 \cdot 9H_2O(aq)$, from the hood.

CAUTION: This iron(III) standard solution has been acidified. Use gloves!

In Table 4-1, record the concentration of Fe^{+3} in this stock solution (as given on the reagent bottle).

2. Rinse a pipet with the iron(III)-containing solution and discard the waste. Using the pipet, carefully transfer 10.00 mL of the iron(III) solution into a 100-mL volumetric flask. Rinse a pipet with some ammonium thiocyanate solution, prepared in Step A.8, and transfer 3 mL of ammonium thiocyanate solution to the same volumetric flask. A red/orange color should develop. To dilute to the 100-mL mark on the volumetric flask:

   a. Use distilled water to dilute the solution to about 1 mL below the mark on the flask, Figure 4-3a.

   b. Thoroughly mix the solution by a) capping the flask; b) holding the cap in place with gloved hand; and c) inverting the flask 10 times, Figure 4-3b.

   c. Now, dilute to the mark on the flask (bottom of meniscus at the line, Figure 4-3c), cover, and thoroughly mix. This solution is your standard solution (i.e., a solution of known concentration).

   d. Dilution and/or mixing is sometimes accompanied by volume expansion. This method of diluting (to about 1 mL below the mark first) allows for volume expansion prior to dilution to final volume.

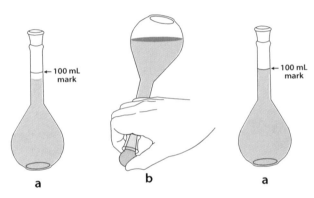

Figure 4-3: a) How you should dilute to 1 mL below the mark; b) How you should cap the flask and invert to mix; c) How you should dilute to the mark.

3. Rinse the colorimeter vial with a small amount of the standard solution in the flask. Transfer enough of the standard solution to nearly fill the colorimeter vial. Cap the vial, wipe off the outside with a Kimwipe, and place it in the colorimeter. Do NOT push the green button on the colorimeter! Record the absorbance of blue light of the standard solution in Table 4-1. This absorbance value must be be-tween 0.3 and 0.9. If it is not, consult your Teaching Assistant. Complete Table 4-1 to determine the proportionality constant between the concentration of iron(III) in the standard solution and the absorbance (see Introduction on pages 30–31). In the next part of the procedure, you will use this proportionality constant to determine the amount of iron in your sample.

   • When calculating the concentration of the standard solution, be sure to account for the 10:100 dilution!

D. ANALYSIS OF THE SAMPLE

1. Empty the 100-mL volumetric flask, and carefully and completely remove all traces of the standard solution.

2. Using filter paper and a Büchner funnel, vacuum filter the solution containing your disintegrated tablet into a clean vacuum flask.

The vacuum flask must be exceptionally clean as contamination will throw off your results. During the filtering process, be sure to clamp the Büchner funnel assembly to prevent it from falling.

3. Gently pour your solution out using your glass stir rod. Let your magnetic stir bar gently fall into the funnel. Fish out your stir bar using tweezers and rinse it off with distilled water, making sure everything ends up back on the filter paper. *At this point, the solution contains dissolved iron(III) from the vitamin tablet and it is the solution that must be retained for analysis.* Once the solution has passed through the filter paper, use 10 mL of distilled water to rinse the Erlenmeyer flask that initially contained your vitamin sample. Also pour this rinse solution through the filter paper to remove the last traces of your sample. Pour the filtrate solution into the 100-mL volumetric flask. Rinse the last vestiges of the filtrate solution from the vacuum flask using 3 mL of distilled water. Pour this rinse solution into the volumetric flask. Pipet 3 mL of the ammonium thiocyanate solution into the volumetric flask. Using the procedure in Part C, Step 2 for **diluting to the mark**, carefully dilute to the mark with distilled water, cover, and mix completely. The solution in the flask should be red. This is "Solution 1."

    CAUTION: This solution, although diluted, will still be very acidic and potentially dangerous. Make sure to use gloves, goggles, and aprons.

4. Rinse the colorimeter vial with a small amount of Solution 1 and then transfer enough of Solution 1 to nearly fill the colorimeter vial (if necessary, use your eye dropper). Cap the vial and place it in the colorimeter. Record the absorbance of blue light by the solution in Table 4-2 in the "Solution 1" box. Don't worry about the last column in Table 4-2 for now; that column will be completed during data analysis.

5. If the absorbance of the solution is between 0.1 and 0.9, then skip directly to Part E. If the absorbance of the solution is greater than 0.9, then you will need to serially dilute your sample until you get a reading between 0.1 and 0.9, as described following.

6. Transfer the solution from the volumetric flask into a clean beaker. Rigorously clean the volumetric flask, as you did after analyzing the standard.

7. Transfer 20.00 mL of Solution 1 into the volumetric flask, using a graduated cylinder. Carefully dilute to the mark, using the **diluting to the mark** procedure, with distilled water before covering and mixing completely. This is "Solution 2."

8. Measure the absorbance of blue light by Solution 2. If the absorbance of the solution is greater than 0.1 and less than 0.9, then skip directly to Part E. If the absorbance of the solution is greater than 0.9, then you will need to continue to serially dilute your sample until you get a reading between 0.1 and 0.9.

9. The third dilution (using 20.00 mL of Solution 2) will produce "Solution 3," etc., until you achieve a solution with an absorbance between 0.1 and 0.9.

E. DATA ANALYSIS

1. Identify which of your solutions had an absorbance between 0.1 and 0.9. Using the proportionality constant you calculated in Table 4-1, calculate the concentration of Fe3+ in that solution. Fill in this value in the proper location on Table 4-2.

2. Calculate $[Fe^{3+}]$ for the other solutions in Table 4-2, moving up the table from your known values. You will have to consider your dilution procedures for this calculation. For instance, taking 20 mL from a solution and diluting it into 100 mL of water would be a 1:5 dilution. Thus, the solution from which the 20 mL came from would be 5 times as concentrated as the new solution.

3. Once you have determined $[Fe^{3+}]$ for Solution 1, complete Table 4-3. You will need to use the fact that the volume of Solution 1 was 100 mL.

4. Double-check all of your calculations and significant figures. Have your Teaching Assistant verify by signing your completion of this experiment. Tear off and hand in the Data Report Sheet for grading. Students working in pairs should include their partner's name on the Data Report Sheet. Dispose of all chemical wastes as indicated by your Teaching Assistant.

Calculations: Show your calculations below. Watch your units and report all answers with the correct number of significant figures.

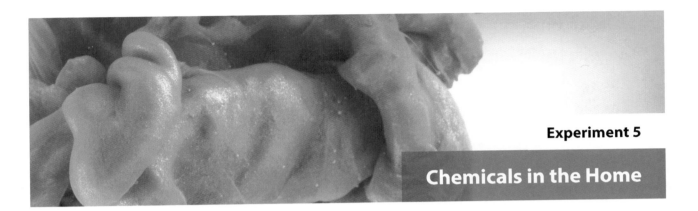

Experiment 5

Chemicals in the Home

- Chemical splash goggles, gloves, and apron must be worn at all times.

- H_2SO_4, NaOH, and bleach solutions are extremely caustic and/or corrosive. Immediately wash all spills with excess water and inform the Teaching Assistant.

- Use two small, clean, dry beakers to obtain minimal amounts (~10 mL) of concentrated H_2SO_4 and NaOH. Label and share these chemicals with a neighbor.

- Only the Teaching Assistant is to dispense the concentrated H_2SO_4 from the reagent bottle!

- Add concentrated H_2SO_4 one drop at a time to a solid. This minimizes the chance of chemicals bubbling over the top and onto your hands.

- Carry out reactions and heating under the student hood to minimize exposure to noxious fumes. Ensure the student hood is firmly seated against the rubber gasket.

- When smelling chemicals, gently waft the fumes toward the nose with your hand or a piece of paper.

Materials List

- household cleaner, with ammonia (NH_3)
- 1.0 M ammonium chloride, NH_4Cl
- 8.0 M sodium hydroxide, NaOH
- garden fertilizer, containing ammonium
- smelling salts, $(NH_4)_2CO_3$
- baking soda, $NaHCO_3$
- 3 M and 18 M sulfuric acid, H_2SO_4
- vinegar, containing acetic acid ($HC_2H_3O_2$)
- limestone, $CaCO_3$
- barium hydroxide, $Ba(OH)_2$ (saturated soln.)

- sodium chloride, NaCl
- 0.10 M silver nitrate, $AgNO_3$
- 14.8 M or concentrated ammonia, NH_3
- epsom salts, containing magnesium sulfate heptahydrate ($MgSO_4 \cdot 7H_2O$)
- 0.20 M barium chloride, $BaCl_2$
- sodium iodide, NaI
- bleach

Objectives

After completing this project, you will be able to:

- recognize chemicals found in common household chemicals.
- predict products of reactions and write balanced equations.
- use chemical properties to identify chemicals found in the home.

Introduction

Preliminary and Confirmatory Tests

Chemicals serve a variety of purposes in the home, from cleaning agents to medicine. Unfortunately, some-times dangerous chemicals are ingested by infants. Therefore, often the rapid identification of such a substance may be the critical factor in saving the infant's life. Chemicals are identified through the use of instruments and/or by characteristic reactions of that substance. Characteristic reactions of chemicals are called "preliminary" or "spot" tests. For example, the preliminary test for hydrogen with a smoldering wooden splint results in a characteristic small explosion or "pop" when hydrogen gas is present. A preliminary test for Ag^+ is the addition of dilute HCl, which results in the formation of a white precipitate of silver(I)chloride (AgCl) if Ag^+ is present. However, since Pb^{+2} and Hg_2^{+2} also yield white precipitates of $PbCl_2$ and Hg_2Cl_2, respectively, upon addition of dilute HCl, a confirmatory test is often needed to clarify the nature of the unknown. In the case of AgCl, addition of aqueous[1] NH_3 will result in the disappearance of the white precipitate. Conversely, addition of aqueous NH_3 will not cause the disappearance of white precipitates of $PbCl_2$ and Hg_2Cl_2. In summary, preliminary tests are used to separate or identify groups of chemicals whereas confirmatory tests are used to separate or identify individual chemicals.

In this experiment, you will perform certain tests on chemicals found in most homes: salt, bleach, baking soda, etc. After performing the tests and recording the results, you will attempt to identify a component in an unknown, i.e. (NH_4^+, I^-, Cl^-, SO_4^{-2}, or CO_3^{-2}). It should be noted that combinations of household chemicals can sometimes lead to explosions or the production of toxic gases. For example, ammonia cleaning solutions should NEVER be mixed with chlorine bleaches due to the formation of acrid fumes of chloramines.

Scientific Background

Ammonia (NH_3) and Ammonium (NH_4^+) Salts

An aqueous solution of ammonia is weakly basic because it contains a low concentration of hydroxide (OH^-) ions. The hydroxide ions are formed during the equilibrium reaction (1). Red litmus paper is used to test for the presence of basicity. The chemical dye in red litmus paper turns blue when exposed to a high enough concentration of hydroxide ions.[2]

$$NH_3\,(g, aq) \;+\; H_2O(l) \;\rightleftharpoons\; NH_4^+(aq) \;+\; OH^-(aq) \tag{1}$$

---

1 Aqueous means dissolved in water.

2 Likewise, blue litmus paper is used to test for the presence of acidity. The chemical dye in blue litmus paper turns red when exposed to a high enough concentration of H^+ (or H_3O^+).

Many substances, including fertilizer and smelling salts, $(NH_4)_2CO_3$, contain ammonium (NH_4^+). Ammonium salts are converted to ammonia by the addition of a strong base (containing hydroxide, OH^-) such as NaOH. This reaction is shown in (2) and is the reverse of the reaction shown in (1).

$$NH_4^+(aq) \ + \ OH^-(aq) \ \rightleftharpoons \ NH_3(g, aq) \ + \ H_2O(l) \tag{2}$$

Thus, a preliminary test for NH_4^+ is to add dilute NaOH to the suspected NH_4^+ containing sample. If the characteristic odor of gaseous NH_3 is sensed, then NH_4^+ is present. A confirmatory test would be to test the basicity of the escaping gas with moist, red litmus. A positive result would confirm the presence of NH_4^+ in the original sample since only NH_3 yields a positive result with this test.

Some ammonium salts, such as $(NH_4)_2CO_3$, are rather unstable and decompose on heating to yield NH_3 as shown in (3).

$$(NH_4)_2CO_3(s) \ \xrightarrow{\Delta} \ 2\,NH_3(g) \ + \ H_2O(g) \ + \ CO_2(g) \tag{3}$$

Baking Soda (NaHCO₃) and Carbonates (CO₃⁻²)

Baking soda is essentially 100% sodium bicarbonate ($NaHCO_3$), while baking powder contains a mixture of $NaHCO_3$ and dry acids (e.g., cream of tartar, tartaric acid, or sodium aluminum sulfate). Many substances, including limestone, sea shells, egg shells, etc., contain carbonate (CO_3^{-2}). Substances that contain HCO_3^- or CO_3^{-2} yield the colorless gas CO_2 upon addition of acids (H^+ containing substance). These reactions are shown in equations (4) and (5), respectively.

$$HCO_3^-(aq) \ + \ H^+(aq) \ \rightleftharpoons \ H_2O(l) \ + \ CO_2(g) \tag{4}$$

$$CO_3^{-2}(aq) \ + \ 2\,H^+(aq) \ \rightleftharpoons \ H_2O(l) \ + \ CO_2(g) \tag{5}$$

Thus a preliminary test for HCO_3^- or CO_3^{-2} is addition of acid to the suspected carbonate-containing sample. However, since Cl^- also yields the colorless gas HCl upon addition of acid, a confirmatory test is needed. A confirmatory test for HCO_3^- or CO_3^{-2} involves testing the escaping gas for the presence of CO_2. The escaping gas is allowed to react with $Ba(OH)_2$. If the escaping gas is CO_2, then a white precipitate of $BaCO_3$ is produced as shown in equation (6).

$$CO_2(g) \ + \ Ba(OH)_2(aq) \ \rightarrow \ BaCO_3(s) \ + \ H_2O(l) \tag{6}$$

Table Salt (NaCl)

All chloride salts (NaCl, $BaCl_2$, $FeCl_3$, etc.) react with concentrated H_2SO_4 to yield hydrogen chloride (HCl), a colorless gas with a stinging odor (see equation 7).

$$NaCl(s) \ + \ H_2SO_4(aq) \ \rightarrow \ NaHSO_4(aq) \ + \ HCl(g) \tag{7}$$

Since HCl is an acid, the escaping gas will turn moist blue litmus paper red. Addition of H_2SO_4 to the suspected chloride containing salt is the preliminary test for Cl^-. The confirmatory tests for Cl^- are precipitation by Ag^+ to form a white precipitate of AgCl and subsequent disappearance of the precipitate in aqueous NH_3. Solid AgCl dissolves in aqueous NH_3 due to the formation of the soluble silver ammonia complex, $[Ag(NH_3)_2]^+$ (see reaction 8).

$$AgCl(s) \ + \ 2\,NH_3(aq) \ \rightarrow \ [Ag(NH_3)_2]^+(aq) \ + \ Cl^-(aq) \tag{8}$$

Epsom Salts (MgSO$_4$·7H$_2$O)

Epsom salts are often used to soak tired feet or aching muscles. Sulfate (SO$_4^{-2}$) containing salts react with aqueous BaCl$_2$ to yield BaSO$_4$, a white precipitate. Thus, addition of BaCl$_2$ to the suspected sulfate containing salt is the confirmatory test for SO$_4^{-2}$.

Bleach (Cl$_2$ Water)

Modern liquid bleaches are about 5% NaOCl in H$_2$O (95% of the stuff you buy is NaCl and H$_2$O). The solution, however, behaves as if Cl$_2$ were dissolved in it. Cl$_2$ is a pale yellow-green, toxic gas with a very irritating odor and is soluble in H$_2$O; hence, the use of NaOCl as a substitute in bleach. Chlorine will liberate a red-brown/black solid of iodine (I$_2$) from salts containing the I$^-$ ion (9).

$$Cl_2(aq) \ + \ 2\,NaI(aq) \ \rightarrow \ I_2(s, aq) \ + \ 2\,NaCl(aq) \qquad\qquad (9)$$

Thus, addition of NaI to the suspected Cl$_2$ (or NaOCl) containing solution is the confirmatory test.

Iodized Salt (I$^-$)

Most table salt purchased at the store is "iodized," meaning that a small amount (0.006–0.01%) of KI has been added. Iodide (I$^-$) is essential for the normal functioning of the thyroid gland. An iodide-containing salt, such as NaI or KI, will react with bleach to liberate the red-brown/black solid I$_2$, as shown in (9). Solid NaI or KI will also react with concentrated H$_2$SO$_4$ to liberate a red-brown/black solid of I$_2$, as well as a purple gas of I$_2$. Although preliminary identification of I$^-$ is almost certainly obtained from the colors produced in either of these tests, it is always best to do a confirmatory test. The confirmatory test for I$^-$ is precipitation by Ag$^+$; a yellow precipitate of AgI confirms the presence of I$^-$.

> **NOTE**
>
> During the course of this experiment and before performing each reaction, use your ability to predict products and your knowledge of the solubility rules to forecast what should occur.

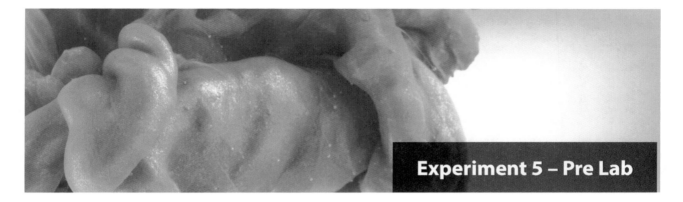

1. The substances or solutions shown in a–h are to be reacted during the course of this experiment. For each: predict chemical formulas for all products, write a balanced chemical reaction (*include physical states*), and predict what should be observed experimentally (colorless gas evolved, precipitate formed, ammonia smell, etc.). Hint: Refer back to the introductory information.

    a. Solid smelling salts and aqueous sodium hydroxide

      (Note: Ammonium hydroxide, NH_4OH, does not exist in solution but decomposes to gaseous ammonia and water.)

      Products?

      _____

      Balanced chemical equation?

      _____

      Predicted experimental observations?

      _____

    b. Solid baking soda and aqueous vinegar (acetic acid, $HC_2H_3O_2$, is active component in vinegar)

      (Note: Carbonic acid, H_2CO_3, does not exist in solution but decomposes to carbon dioxide gas and water.)

      Products?

      _____

      Balanced chemical equation?

      _____

      Predicted experimental observations?

      _____

    c. Limestone ($CaCO_3$) and concentrated sulfuric acid

      Products?

      _____

      Balanced chemical equation?

      _____

      Predicted experimental observations?

      _____

d. Solid table salt and concentrated sulfuric acid

Products?

_____

Balanced chemical equation?

_____

Predicted experimental observations?

_____

e. Aqueous solutions of table salt and silver nitrate

Products?

_____

Balanced chemical equation?

_____

Predicted experimental observations?

_____

f. Aqueous solutions of Epsom salts and barium chloride

Products?

_____

Balanced chemical equation?

_____

Predicted experimental observations?

_____

g. Aqueous solutions of bleach and sodium iodide

Products?

_____

Balanced chemical equation?

_____

Predicted experimental observations?

_____

h. Aqueous solutions of sodium iodide and silver nitrate

Products?

_____

Balanced chemical equation?

_____

Predicted experimental observations?

_____

Procedure

Characteristic Preliminary and Confirmatory Tests

Students are to work individually on all parts of this experiment. However, you are welcome to compare and contrast your experimental results and share chemicals (properly labeled) with your neighbor. As you complete the experiment, record all of your experimental data (observations/product chemical formulas) within your laboratory manual.

A. AMMONIA

1. Obtain about 5 mL of a household cleaner containing ammonia. Hold a piece of dry red litmus paper over the beaker, being careful not to touch the sides of the beaker. Record any color change. Note the distinctive smell of ammonia.

2. Repeat the above using a wet piece of red litmus paper. If a color change is observed, what does this indicate? Record your observations, noting any difference in time (faster or slower) required for the color change.

3. Place about 1 mL of 1.0 M NH_4Cl solution in a small test tube and hold a piece of wet red litmus paper over the mouth of the test tube. **NOTE: When working with small test tubes, use test tube clamps to hold the test tube.** Record your observations.

4. Now, add 1 mL of 8.0 M NaOH to the NH_4Cl solution. Hold a piece of wet red litmus paper over the mouth. Gently waft any fumes toward your nose. Do you detect the smell of ammonia? Record your observations and predict chemical formulas for any products formed. If nothing is observed, you may need to warm (use a hot plate on low setting, do not boil) the solution in order to obtain a positive test. **CAUTIONS: When heating, remember to point the mouth of the test tube away from your-self and your neighbor. NaOH is caustic and corrosive. Wash spills with lots of water and inform the Teaching Assistant.** Try this same test on a 0.5-g sample (about a match head) of a garden fertilizer and on smelling salts, $(NH_4)_2CO_3$. Record your observations and predict products.

5. Some ammonium salts are rather unstable and decompose to yield NH_3. Determine if a solid sample of smelling salts, $(NH_4)_2CO_3$, has the characteristic odor of NH_3.

Observations

a. Household ammonia: Effect on dry litmus? _____

b. Household ammonia: Effect on wet litmus? _____

c. NH_4Cl: Effect on wet litmus? _____

d. NH_4Cl + NaOH: Effect on wet litmus? _____

   d.1 Chemical formulas of products? _____

e. Fertilizer + NaOH: Effect on wet litmus? _____

f. $(NH_4)_2CO_3$ + NaOH: Effect on wet litmus? _____

   f.1 Chemical formulas of products? _____

B. BAKING SODA (NaHCO$_3$) AND CARBONATES (CO$_3^{-2}$)

1. Place a small amount (about the size of a BB) of baking soda in a test tube. Add one or two drops of dilute 3 M H$_2$SO$_4$. **CAUTION: H$_2$SO$_4$ is caustic and corrosive. Wash spills with lots of water and inform the Teaching Assistant.** Record your observations and predict products.

2. Repeat the above using vinegar in place of the H$_2$SO$_4$. The active component in vinegar is acetic acid (HC$_2$H$_3$O$_2$), a weak acid. Record your observations and predict products.

3. Place a small piece of limestone (about 1 cm) in a dry test tube. Carefully add one to two drops of dilute 3 M H$_2$SO$_4$. Test the escaping gas for CO$_2$ by carefully holding a drop of Ba(OH)$_2$ solution, suspended from a medicine dropper, halfway down the test tube. Observe any changes in the drop. If the drop turns cloudy, what does this indicate? Record your observations and predict products.

		Chemical Formulas of Products	Observations
a.	Baking soda + dil. H$_2$SO$_4$?	_____	_____
b.	Baking soda + vinegar?	_____	_____
c.	Limestone + dil. H$_2$SO$_4$?	_____	_____
d.	Escaping gas + Ba(OH)$_2$?	_____	_____

C. TABLE SALT (NaCl)

1. Place a small amount (about the size of a BB) of NaCl in a test tube. Add one or two drops of concentrated 18 M H$_2$SO$_4$. **CAUTION: Concentrated H$_2$SO$_4$ is caustic and corrosive. Wash spills with lots of water and inform the Teaching Assistant.** Carefully hold a piece of moist, blue litmus over the test tube. Record your observations. Predict chemical formulas of products.

2. Place a small amount of NaCl in a test tube and then add about 15 drops of distilled water to dissolve the NaCl. Next, add three to four drops of 0.10 M AgNO$_3$. If a precipitate forms, indicate so under your observations and record the color of the precipitate. Predict the chemical formulas of products.

3. Use the centrifuge to pull the precipitate formed in Step 2 to the bottom of the test tube. Discard the supernatant liquid. To the precipitate, add 6 drops of concentrated 14.8 M NH$_3$ and stir. Record your observations.

4. Place about 15 drops of Morgantown's tap water in a test tube. Add about 10 drops of 0.10 M AgNO$_3$. Stir and allow it to stand for at least one minute. Note whether the solution becomes cloudy, indicating formation of a precipitate. Record your observations.

		Chemical Formulas of Products	Observations
a.	Salt + conc. H$_2$SO$_4$?	_____	_____
b.	Salt + AgNO$_3$?	_____	_____
c.	AgCl(s) + conc. NH$_3$?	_____	_____
d.	Tap water + AgNO$_3$?	_____	_____

D. EPSOM SALTS (MgSO₄·7H₂O)

1. Place a small amount (about the size of a match head) of Epsom salts in a test tube. Add one or two drops of dilute 3 M H_2SO_4. Record your observations and predict chemical formulas of products (if any). Take special note of the difference between this reaction and that of baking soda with H_2SO_4. Does a reaction occur between Epsom salts and H_2SO_4? Explain.

2. Place a small amount of Epsom salts in a test tube and then add 1–2 mL of distilled water to dissolve the Epsom salts. Next, add one or two drops of 0.20 M $BaCl_2$. Record your observations. Predict chemical formulas of products.

	Chemical Formulas of Products	Observations
a. Epsom salts + dil. H_2SO_4?	_____	_____
b. Epsom salts + $BaCl_2$?	_____	_____

E. BLEACH (Cl₂ WATER)

1. Place a small amount (about the size of a match head) of NaI in a test tube and then add about 1 mL of distilled water to dissolve. Add five drops of bleach. **CAUTION: Bleach is caustic, corrosive, and decolorizes clothing. Wash spills with lots of water and inform the Teaching Assistant.** Record your observations. Predict chemical formulas of products.

	Chemical Formula of Products	Observations
a. Bleach + NaI?	_____	_____

F. IODIZED SALT (I⁻)

1. Place a small amount (about the size of a BB) of NaI in a test tube and then add about 1 mL of distilled water to dissolve. Add one or two drops of 0.10 M $AgNO_3$. Record your observations. Predict chemical formulas of products.

2. Place a small amount of NaI in a test tube and carefully add one or two drops of concentrated 18 M H_2SO_4. Record your observations.

	Chemical Formulas of Products	Observations
a. NaI + $AgNO_3$?	_____	_____
b. NaI + conc. H_2SO_4?	_____	_____

Procedure:

Analysis of Unknown Household Chemical

A. UNKNOWN (CONTAINS ONE OF THE FOLLOWING IONS: NH_4^+, I^-, Cl^-, SO_4^{2-}, OR CO_3^{2-})

1. Place a small amount (about the size of a match head) of your unknown in a test tube. Carefully add one or two drops of concentrated 18 M H_2SO_4. **CAUTION: Add concentrated H_2SO_4 one drop at a time to minimize the chance of chemicals bubbling over the top and onto your hands.** Record your observations. Did a purple vapor form? Was a colorless gas evolved?

2. Using the flowchart shown on the next page, perform the appropriate confirmatory test. Record your observations.

3. Fill in the Experiment 5 Data Report Sheet and have your Teaching Assistant verify, by signing, your completion of this experiment. Rip off and hand in the Data Report Sheet for grading. Each student is to hand in his/her own Data Report Sheet. The report sheet will be graded and then returned at your next laboratory meeting. Dispose of all chemical wastes as indicated by your Teaching Assistant.

Observations

a. Unknown solid + conc. H_2SO_4? _____

b. Confirmatory tests and results? _____

_____

_____

_____

_____

_____

c. Unknown ion? _____

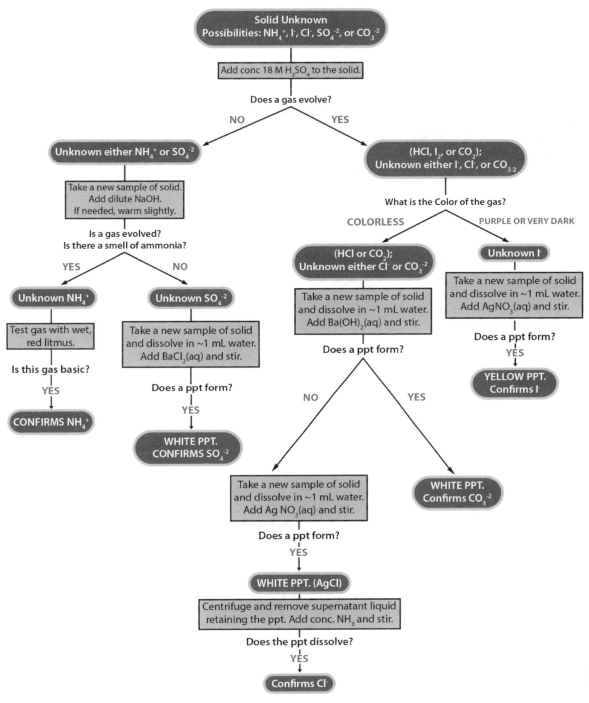

Solid Unknown
Possibilities: NH_4^+, I^-, Cl^-, SO_4^{-2}, or CO_3^{-2}

Add conc 18 M H_2SO_4 to the solid.

Does a gas evolve?

NO / **YES**

NO: Unknown either NH_4^+ or SO_4^{-2}

Take a new sample of solid.
Add dilute NaOH.
If needed, warm slightly.

Is a gas evolved?
Is there a smell of ammonia?

YES / **NO**

YES: Unknown NH_4^+

Test gas with wet, red litmus.

Is this gas basic?

YES

CONFIRMS NH_4^+

NO: Unknown SO_4^{-2}

Take a new sample of solid and dissolve in ~1 mL water. Add $BaCl_2$(aq) and stir.

Does a ppt form?

YES

WHITE PPT. CONFIRMS SO_4^{-2}

YES: (HCl, I_2, or CO_2);
Unknown either I^-, Cl^-, or CO_{3-2}

What is the Color of the gas?

COLORLESS / **PURPLE OR VERY DARK**

COLORLESS: (HCl or CO_2);
Unknown either Cl^- or CO_3^{-2}

Take a new sample of solid and dissolve in ~1 mL water. Add $Ba(OH)_2$(aq) and stir.

Does a ppt form?

NO / **YES**

YES: **WHITE PPT. Confirms CO_3^{-2}**

NO: Take a new sample of solid and dissolve in ~1 mL water. Add Ag NO_3(aq) and stir.

Does a ppt form?

YES

WHITE PPT. (AgCl)

Centrifuge and remove supernatant liquid retaining the ppt. Add conc. NH_3 and stir.

Does the ppt dissolve?

YES

Confirms Cl^-

PURPLE OR VERY DARK: Unknown I^-

Take a new sample of solid and dissolve in ~1 mL water. Add $AgNO_3$(aq) and stir.

Does a ppt form?

YES

YELLOW PPT. Confirms I^-

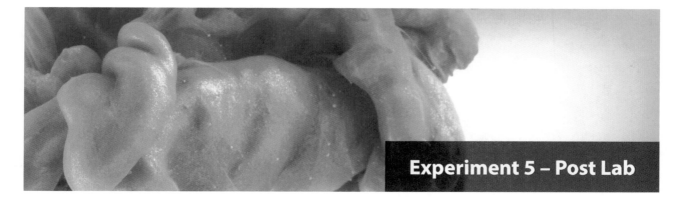

1. Use your knowledge of solubility rules and predicting products of chemical reactions to answer the following questions.

   a. An unknown solid contained either Na_2CO_3 or NH_4NO_3. The unknown solid gave off a gas when 3–4 drops of concentrated H_2SO_4 was added. Is the unknown solid Na_2CO_3 or NH_4NO_3? What is the chemical identity of the gas evolved? What confirmatory test could be used?

   b. An unknown solid contained either K_2CO_3 or KI. An aqueous solution of the unknown solid produced a white precipitate when 3–4 drops of $Ba(OH)_2$ was added. Is the unknown solid K_2CO_3 or KI? What is the chemical identity of the white precipitate?

   c. An unknown solid contained either NaCl or NH_4NO_3. An aqueous solution of the unknown solid produced a precipitate upon addition of $AgNO_3(aq)$. Is the unknown solid NaCl or NH_4NO_3? What is the chemical identity of the precipitate? What confirmatory test could be used?

   d. An unknown solid contained either K_2CO_3 or Na_2SO_4. An aqueous solution of the unknown solid produced a white precipitate upon addition of $BaCl_2(aq)$. Is the unknown solid K_2CO_3 or Na_2SO_4? Is addition of $BaCl_2$ a good method for distinguishing CO_3^{-2} from SO_4^{-2}? Why or why not?

   e. An unknown solid contained either Na_2SO_4 or NH_4ClO_4. The unknown solid gave off a gas when 3–4 drops of dilute NaOH was added. Is the unknown solid Na_2SO_4 or NH_4ClO_4? What is the chemical identity of the gas? What confirmatory test could be used?

2. Describe a method for distinguishing between the following solids:

    a. table salt and Epsom salts

    b. smelling salts and baking soda

    c. table salt and sodium iodide

3. Describe one or more tests that could distinguish solutions of the following chemicals:

    a. $(NH_4)_2CO_3$ and NaCl

    b. NaI and $NaHCO_3$

    c. bleach and ammonia

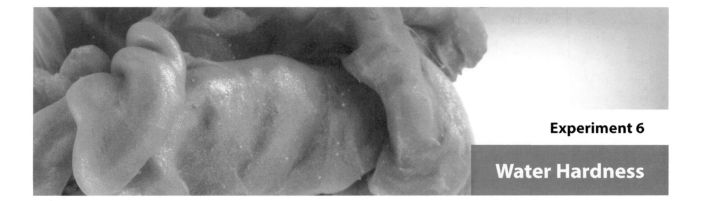

- Chemical splash goggles, gloves, and apron must be worn at all times.
- Tie back long hair and loose sleeves.

Materials List

- standard soap solution
- disodium salt of ethylenediaminetetraacetic acid (Na_2EDTA) solution
- ammonia/ammonium chloride buffer solution, NH_3/NH_4Cl
- Eriochrome Black T indicator

Objectives

- After completing this project, you will be able to:
- properly conduct a titration using an indicator to signify the end point.
- determine total hardness in water by titration using both standard soap and EDTA solutions.
- discuss and explain: ions responsible for hard water, i.e., hardness ions, problems associated with hard water use, hard vs. soft water and reasons for decreased cleansing ability in hard water, and methods of converting hard water to soft water.
- calculate total hardness in water in units of parts per million and molarity.
- derive and explain the relationship between the various definitions of parts per million.

Introduction

Soap

Sodium stearate, $C_{17}H_{35}CO_2Na$, is the chemical formula for a common soap that will be used to illustrate the effect of the hardness ions on the cleansing ability of soap. Sodium stearate is soluble in water and in the absence of hardness ions dissolves to form the sodium cation and the stearate anion ($C_{17}H_{35}CO_2^-$). The stearate anion, when dissolved in solution, effects the cleansing of oil and dirt from skin and clothing.

The cleansing ability of soap is related to the dual polarity of the stearate anion. The nonpolar hydrocarbon tail is repelled by polar water molecules but is attracted to nonpolar oil droplets (see Figure 6-1). This hydrocarbon tail is designated *hydrophobic* (water-hating).

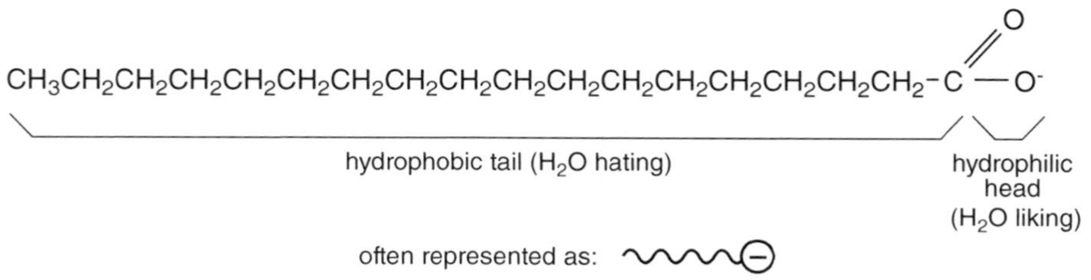

$$CH_3CH_2CH_2CH_2CH_2CH_2CH_2CH_2CH_2CH_2CH_2CH_2CH_2CH_2CH_2CH_2CH_2-C \overset{O}{\diagup} - O^-$$

hydrophobic tail (H$_2$O hating)

hydrophilic head (H$_2$O liking)

often represented as: ∿∿∿⊖

Figure 6-1: Stearate anion.

Conversely, the polar carboxylate head is attracted to the polar water molecules. This carboxylate head is designated *hydrophilic* (water-liking). In order to "cleanse" an oily surface, stearate anions must be free to move around in solution so the nonpolar tails can surround and dissolve in the nonpolar oil droplet. At the same time, the polar heads point outward and remain dissolved in the water. Eventually the oil droplet is pulled from the skin or clothing and completely surrounded by stearate anions in this way. The oil droplet surrounded by hundreds of stearate anions is said to be emulsified; a representation of the emulsified oil droplet or micelle is shown in Figure 6-2. The emulsified oil droplet is soluble in water and is washed away, thus causing the cleansing.

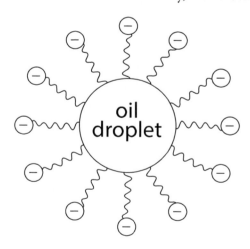

Figure 6-2: Emulsified oil droplet.

Hardness in Water

Hardness in water is caused by the presence of dissolved calcium, magnesium, and iron(II/III) salts. Hardness ions in water react with soap to form insoluble compounds causing a waste of soap. For example, if the sodium stearate soap previously discussed is dissolved in water containing a high concentration of the hardness ion Ca^{2+}, the precipitation reaction shown in (1) will occur.

$$Ca^{2+}(aq) + 2\ C_{17}H_{35}CO_2Na(aq) \longrightarrow Ca(C_{17}H_{35}CO_2)_2(s) + 2\ Na^+(aq) \qquad (1)$$
$$\text{(present in hard water)} \qquad \text{(soap)} \qquad\qquad \text{(soap scum)}$$

Similar precipitation reactions will occur with the other hardness ions. The stearate anion reacts with the Ca^{2+} forming an insoluble precipitate of $Ca(C_{17}H_{35}CO_2)_2$, more commonly known as soap "scum," which results in bathtub rings and dulling of color when laundering wash. Once all hardness ions have been precipitated by the soap in this way, any soap left remains dissolved and can effect the cleansing. As a result, when washing in hard water, a larger quantity of soap must be used; one portion to precipitate the hardness ions and the second portion to effect the cleansing.

Conversion of Hard Water to Soft Water

Hard water can be converted to soft water by removal of the hardness ions. Hardness ions can be removed by precipitation, complexation, and ion exchange. Sodium carbonate (Na_2CO_3) and sodium tetraborate ($Na_2B_4O_7$) are commonly used to remove hardness ions by precipitation reactions. Both form insoluble compounds with Ca^{2+}, Mg^{2+}, and Fe^{2+}, and thus the concentration of ions is reduced. Precipitation reactions with the Mg_2^+ hardness ion are shown in (2) and (3). Similar precipitation reactions occur with the other hardness ions.

$$Mg^{2+}(aq) + Na_2CO_3(aq) \longrightarrow MgCO_3(s) + 2\ Na^+(aq) \qquad (2)$$

$$Mg^{2+}(aq) + Na_2B_4O_7(aq) \longrightarrow MgB_4O_7(s) + 2\ Na^+(aq) \qquad (3)$$

Sodium metaphosphate, $NaPO_3$, removes hardness ions from solution by complexing them as shown in (4). The properties of the complex ion $[Ca(PO_3)_6]^{4-}$ are considerably different from those of Ca^{2+}. In particular, $[Ca(PO_3)_6]^{4-}$ will not react with soap as will Ca^{2+}. However, waste phosphates are environmental pollutants and their use is highly restricted by law. Phosphates are fertilizers and promote plant growth in bodies of water. The plants deplete the supply of dissolved oxygen in the water, which, in turn, results in widespread fish death due to asphyxiation.

$$Ca^{2+}(aq) + 6\ NaPO_3(aq) \longrightarrow [Ca(PO_3)_6]^{4-}(aq) + 6\ Na^+(aq) \qquad (4)$$

A number of natural and synthetic materials will remove ions from solution by the process of ion exchange. In reaction (5), the substance $NaAlSi_2O_6$ is a naturally occurring material called a zeolite. When hard water is passed through a column containing a zeolite, Na^+ in the zeolite is exchanged for Ca^{2+}, Mg^{2+}, or Fe^{3+}, and thus the water is softened. This method is used for softening water in homes.

$$2\ NaAlSi_2O_6(s) + Ca^{2+}(aq) \longrightarrow Ca(AlSi_2O_6)_2(s) + 2\ Na^+(aq) \qquad (5)$$

Scientific Background

Parts Per Million (ppm)

Although chemists customarily express concentrations in molarity, the amount of hardness in water is usually expressed as parts per million (ppm) of $CaCO_3$ in the water. A hardness of 1 ppm $CaCO_3$ means that there is 1 gram of $CaCO_3$ in 1 million grams of aqueous solution (which is mostly water), or that there is 1 milligram of $CaCO_3$ in 1,000 grams of aqueous solution. The relationship between these two definitions of the ppm is shown in (6).

$$1 \text{ ppm } CaCO_3 = \frac{1 \text{ g } CaCO_3}{1,000,000 \text{ g aq soln}} \times \frac{1000 \text{ mg } CaCO_3}{1 \text{ g } CaCO_3}$$

$$= \frac{1 \text{ g } CaCO_3}{1000 \text{ g aq soln}} = \frac{1 \text{ mg } CaCO_3}{1 \text{ kg aq soln}} = \frac{1 \text{ mg } CaCO_3}{1 \text{ L aq soln}} \tag{6}$$

The last definition comes about by assuming that the aqueous solution is dilute and, as a result, the density of the solution is the same as that of pure water, which is 1.00 g/mL.

Classification of water as hard or soft in terms of ppm $CaCO_3$ is somewhat arbitrary. In general, water is classified as soft if the concentration of dissolved salts is less than 100 ppm and hard if the concentration of dissolved salts is greater than 200 ppm. If the hardness is between 100–200 ppm, the water might be classified as moderately hard.

Methods of Determining Water Hardness

In this experiment, two different methods will be used to determine water hardness: 1) titration with soap solution; and 2) titration with EDTA. The soap titration will be discussed first.

It was mentioned previously that hardness ions in water form insoluble compounds with soap (refer back to Equation 1). Thus, soap will not form suds and will not cleanse as long as hardness ions are present. How-ever, once the hardness ions have been removed by precipitation with soap, any excess soap that is added will form suds, which can effect the cleansing. This is the basis for the determination of hardness in water by titration with soap solution. The end point in this titration is the point at which all the hardness ions have been precipitated by the soap, and can be observed visually as the point at which the first permanent suds appear.

The second method for determination of water hardness is by titration with EDTA. EDTA is the abbreviation for *ethylenediaminetetraacetic acid*. The structure of EDTA^{4-} is shown in Figure 6-3. The soap solution precipitates the hardness ions, whereas the EDTA complexes the hardness ions. The EDTA^{4-} ion forms an octahedral complex with the hardness ion by wrapping around and binding to the hardness ion through the six atoms marked with an asterisk in Figure 6-3. This complexation effectively cages (sequesters) the hardness ions such that they are no longer free to react with soap.

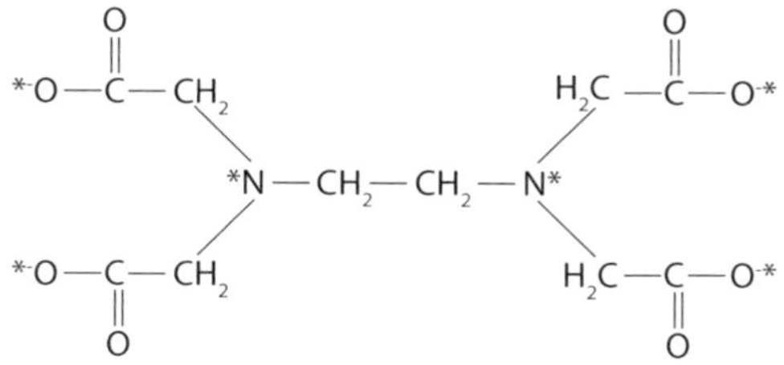

Figure 6-3: Structure of EDTA^{4-}.

As shown in equation (7), one mole of Ca^{2+} or Mg^{2+} reacts with one mole of EDTA to form a very stable complex ion.

$$Ca^{2+}(aq) + EDTA^{4-}(aq) \longrightarrow [Ca(EDTA)]^{2-}(aq) \qquad (7)$$

The end point is detected by use of the indicator Eriochrome Black T. At the start of the titration and in the presence of free Ca^{2+} and Mg^{2+}, this indicator is wine-red in color. At the end point and once all Ca^{2+} and Mg^{2+} have been complexed, this indicator will be blue in color. Thus, the first drop of excess EDTA will cause the color of the indicator to change from wine-red to blue. Throughout the titration, the OH^- concentration must be maintained at about 1×10^{-4} M. This will prevent precipitation of Mg^{2+} as $Mg(OH)_2$. The addition of a NH_3/NH_4^+ buffer solution is used to maintain the OH^- concentration at the proper value. In Part B of this experiment, you will determine the concentration of Ca^{2+} in an unknown solution using an EDTA titration.

Notes on Use of Burets During Titrations

The buret is marked at every 0.1 mL. Read the buret to one place in between the markings (i.e., to the nearest 0.01 mL). Thus, buret readings should be given to two digits past the decimal place. Use the bottom of the meniscus as the reference point for your volume readings.

Burets are made to deliver variable amounts of liquid. During a titration, you are concerned with how much liquid has been delivered and NOT how much liquid remains in the buret. As a result, burets are read from top to bottom and subtraction is used to determine volume delivered as shown below.

Volume of Soln. Delivered = *Current/Final Buret Reading – Initial Buret Reading*

For example, if the initial buret reading is 2.22 mL and the final buret reading is 10.79 mL, then the volume of soln. delivered = 10.79 mL – 2.22 mL = 8.57 mL.

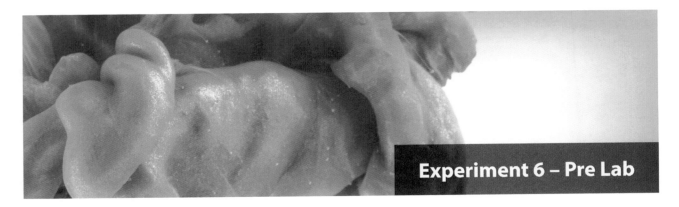

Experiment 6 – Pre Lab

Answer the following questions. Show all work and calculations to support your answers. Include the correct units and the proper number of significant figures on numerical answers. Circle your final answers.

1. A 25.0-mL sample of municipal tap water requires 12.66 mL of soap solution before the appearance of permanent suds. If 1.00 mL of soap solution titrates 0.78 mg $CaCO_3$, what is the ppm $CaCO_3$ in the tap water?

2. What is the molarity of Ca^{2+} in the municipal tap water of the previous question? (Hint: Convert ppm or mg $CaCO_3$/L soln. to M = mol Ca^{2+}/L soln.)

3. Would the municipal tap water be classified as hard or soft water? (Hint: See Scientific Background.)

4. Use dimensional analysis to show that 215 ppm $CaCO_3$ is equivalent to 215 mg $CaCO_3$ per liter of solution. Assume the density of the solution is 1.00 g/mL.

Experiment 6 | Water Hardness   61

Procedure

Do not work in pairs. All students are to work individually and each student must complete all parts of this experiment.

A. TITRATION WITH SOAP SOLUTION

1. Thoroughly clean a 250-mL Erlenmeyer flask and rinse several times with tap water. Using a graduated cylinder, add 50.0 mL of **tap water** to the flask. Record the volume of tap water in the data section.

2. Clean the buret and rinse two times with the soap solution found in the hood. Fill the buret with soap solution. Record the initial buret volume and the concentration of the soap solution.

3. Add about 10 drops of soap solution to the flask, then cork and shake. Continue adding soap solution, 10 drops at a time and shaking after each addition, until permanent suds, which last a minimum of three minutes, appear. The visual observation of permanent suds indicates the end point. Record the final buret volume in the data section.

4. Repeat the titration except substitute 50 mL of **distilled water** for the tap water. Remember to rinse the flask several times with distilled water before placing the sample in it.

5. Calculate the hardness (in ppm $CaCO_3$) for both the tap water and the distilled water. Record these values in the data section. Include all of your calculations on the back of the data page.

   Which sample of water, tap or distilled, is harder? Why?

   _____

   _____

B. EDTA TITRATIONS

6. Thoroughly clean the buret by a) disposing of the soap solution; b) rinsing with copious amounts of tap water; and c) followed by several rinses with distilled water. Rinse the buret several times with EDTA solution. Fill the buret with EDTA solution. Record the initial buret volume and the concentration of the EDTA solution in the data section.

7. Thoroughly clean the Erlenmeyer flask and rinse several times with distilled water. Measure and put 50 mL of **tap water** into the flask. Add 5 mL of buffer solution to the flask and swirl to mix. Add 5 drops of Eriochrome Black T indicator and swirl to mix. **NOTE: The buffer solution must be added before the indicator.**

8. Swirling the flask continuously, titrate with the EDTA solution until the color within the flask changes from **wine-red to true blue.** Wash the sides of the flask occasionally with distilled water from the wash bottle. Read the buret and record the final buret volume in the data section.

9. Calculate the hardness of the tap water as determined from the EDTA titration.

    How does this value compare with the hardness of tap water determined from the soap titration? Which method, soap titration or EDTA titration, is preferable for determining hardness in water?

    _____

    _____

    _____

10. Thoroughly clean the Erlenmeyer flask and rinse several times with distilled water. Thoroughly clean a pipet and rinse with a small amount of your unknown. Your unknown is water of unknown hardness, i.e., ppm $CaCO_3$, and you are to determine its hardness via EDTA titration. Pipet 10.00 mL of your unknown solution into the Erlenmeyer flask. Dilute the unknown with 40 mL of distilled water. Add 5 mL of the buffer followed by 5 drops of the indicator. Titrate with the EDTA solution as described in Step B.3. Repeat the titration. If necessary, repeat the titration a third time. For each titration, calculate the hardness of your unknown as determined from the EDTA titration. Include all of your calculations on the back of the data page.

    Would your unknown water sample be classified as hard or soft water? Based upon this classification, would you want to take a bath in your unknown solution? Why or why not?

    _____

    _____

    _____

11. Double-check all of your calculations, significant figures, and units. Fill in the Experiment 6 Data Report Sheet and have your Teaching Assistant verify your completion of this experiment by signing. Rip off and hand in the Data Report Sheet for grading. Each student is to hand in his/her own Data Report Sheet. The report sheet will be graded and then returned at your next laboratory meeting.

Calculations: Show your calculations below. Watch your units and report all answers with the correct number of significant figures.

Data

A	Titration with Soap Solution	Tap Water	Distilled Water
1	Volume of sample titrated		
2	Final buret volume		
3	Initial buret volume		
4	Volume of soap solution		
5	Concentration of soap solution	_____ mL soap solution = _____ mg CaCO$_3$	
6	mg of CaCO$_3$ in the sample		
7	mg of CaCO$_3$ per mL of sample		
8	ppm CaCO$_3$ in sample = mg of CaCO$_3$ per L of sample or mg of CaCO$_3$ per 1000 g sample		

B	EDTA Titrations	Unknown			
		Tap Water	Trial 1	Trial 2	Trial 3
9	Volume of sample titrated				
10	Final buret volume				
11	Initial buret volume				
12	Volume of EDTA solution				
13	Concentration of EDTA solution	_____ mL EDTA solution = _____ mg CaCO$_3$			
14	mg of CaCO$_3$ in the sample				
15	mg of CaCO$_3$ per mL of sample				
16	ppm CaCO$_3$ in sample = mg of CaCO$_3$ per L of sample or mg of CaCO$_3$ per 1000 g sample				
17	Molarity of Ca^{2+} in sample				

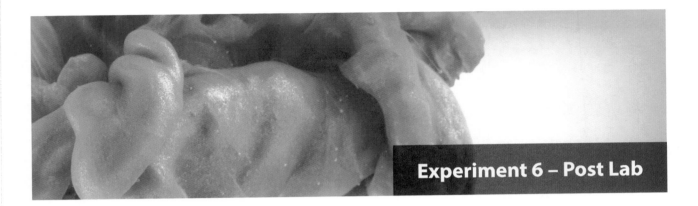

Answer the following questions. Show all work and calculations to support your answers. Include the correct units and the proper number of significant figures on numerical answers. Circle your final answers.

1. Which of the two methods for determining water hardness, titration with soap or EDTA solution, do you believe is better? Why?

2. A 25.0-mL sample of water was titrated with EDTA using Eriochrome Black T as the indicator. The solution became a true blue color after the addition of 5.72 mL of 0.010 M EDTA. Calculate the following:

    a. molarity of Ca^{2+} in the sample (Hint: See Equation 7 in Scientific Background.)

    b. hardness of the water in ppm $CaCO_3$

    c. Would this sample of water be classified as hard or soft?

3. During the determination of ppm $CaCO_3$ in the unknown, 10 mL of unknown was diluted with 40 mL of distilled water. If tap water was mistakenly used in place of distilled water, how would this procedural error affect the calculated value of ppm $CaCO_3$ in the unknown?

4. Write a balanced equation for the reaction of the soap potassium stearate ($C_{17}H_{35}CO_2K$) with magnesium sulfate.

The Kool-Aid Acid Test

SAFETY PRECAUTIONS

- Chemical splash goggles, gloves, and apron must be worn at all times.
- Wear gloves when handling chemicals and performing a titration.
- Acid and base solutions are corrosive. Immediately wash all spills with excess water and inform the teaching assistant.
- Don't drink the Kool-Aid!

Materials List

- 0.70 M sodium hydroxide, NaOH
- phenolphthalein indicator solution
- drink mix powders

Objectives

After completing this project, you will be able to:

- perform an acid-base titration.
- calculate an acid or base concentration from titration data.
- express composition in terms of percent composition.

Introduction

The human stomach is a strongly acidic environment. The main component present in the human stomach during digestion is hydrochloric acid (HCl) leading to a pH of 1-2. Consumption of strongly basic substances will neutralize acid in the stomach and interfere with digestion. Because of this fact, most natural foods are either neutral or acidic. Therefore, artificial foods must have a compatibly low (acidic) pH. In most commercially-available instant drink mixes, the majority of the mass is an organic acid, such as citric acid ($C_6H_8O_7$). Since citric acid has three acidic protons (H^+), the chemical formula for citric acid is often written as $H_3C_6H_5O_7$. This focuses attention on the three acidic protons. Acidic protons are highlighted in bold on the structural formula for citric acid below.

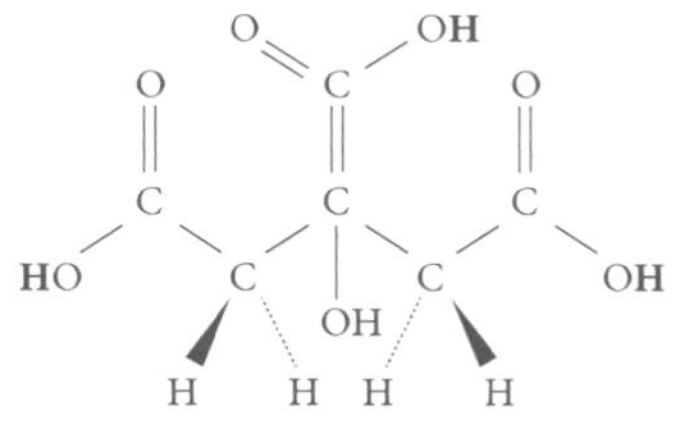

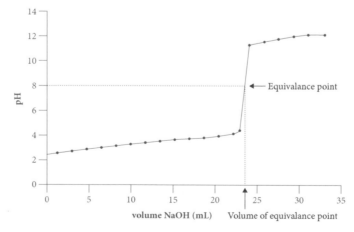

Figure 7-1: Citric acid structural formula: acidic protons are highlighted in bold

Quality control is an essential and important process in the production of such drink mixes. The composition of the mix must be monitored constantly to ensure that the consumer receives a consistent product. You will take the role of a quality-control chemist and analyze the composition of several packages of Kool-Aid to determine their consistency. You will then analyze another drink mix in order to compare its acid content.

Scientific Background

In this experiment, you will monitor the pH of a Kool-Aid solution while a basic solution is added to it. The Kool-Aid is acidic, so the pH will start low (below 7). As the basic solution is added, the acid will be neutralized and the pH will rise. The shape of the "pH versus volume of base" plot will allow you to determine the amount of acid that was in the Kool-Aid. This general procedure is called "titration," and is used extensively when analyzing acids and bases, as well as some other types of compounds.

Figure 7-2: Titration curve of a citric acid solution titrated with 0.40 M NaOH

A titration curve is generated by plotting the pH of an acid solution versus total volume (in mL) of strong base added. A typical titration curve is shown in *Figure 7-2*.

A *neutralization reaction* typically involves an acid and base reacting to produce a salt and water as shown in (1). The neutralization reaction between citric acid ($H_3C_6H_5O_7$) and the strong base NaOH is shown in equation (2). As NaOH is added, it reacts with the acid $H_3C_6H_5O_7$ to produce the salt of the acid, $Na_3C_6H_5O_7$, and water.

$$\text{acid} \quad + \quad \text{base} \quad \longrightarrow \quad \text{salt} \quad + \quad \text{water} \tag{1}$$

$$H_3C_6H_5O_7 \quad + \quad 3\,NaOH(aq) \quad \longrightarrow \quad Na_3C_6H_5O_7(aq) \quad + \quad 3\,H_2O(l) \tag{2}$$

Notice that citric acid is *triprotic*: each molecule has *three acidic protons (H^+)*. If NaOH is the limiting reagent (limits amount of product formed), then after the neutralization reaction occurs there will be citric acid remaining, and the solution will be acidic. If citric acid is the limiting reagent, then after the neutralization reaction occurs there will be NaOH base remaining, and the solution will be basic.

Therefore (this is important!):

- **Immediately before complete neutralization, the pH will be acidic (pH < 7).**
- **Immediately after complete neutralization, the pH will be basic (pH > 7).**
- **At the point of neutralization ("equivalence") the pH will suddenly jump (by 4 pH units or more).**

  *The **equivalence point** is defined as the point in the titration where stoichiometric amounts of both reagents are present (i.e., enough base has been added to neutralize all of the add).*

Here is one of the most useful properties of a titration: around when the acid and base are in *exact* stoichiometric proportions (at the equivalence point), the pH rises suddenly. The *equivalence point* is the *inflection point* within this region of sharply rising pH. Look back at *Figure 7-2* and find the equivalence point. If you can locate this point, you'll have stoichiometric information.

Titration Monitored by Indicator

Another method of detecting the equivalence point is through the use of colored indicator compounds. Indicators change color at a specific pH value, called the end point of the titration. Phenolphthalein (pronounced feen-ol-fthay-leen!) is colorless in acidic solutions, and pink in basic solutions. The color change occurs around pH 9. Phenolphthalein will be used in the experimental procedure as a second method of locating the equivalence point. Before coming to the laboratory, watch the videos http:/www.youtube.com/watch?v=9DkB82xLvNE and http://www.youtube.com/watch?v=g8jdCWC10vQ on doing a titration using an indicator and on doing a titration using a pH meter, respectively.

> *The **end point** is defined as the point in the titration where the indicator changes color. A properly chosen indicator has an endpoint that occurs at or about the same pH as the equivalence point.*

Notes on Use of Burets During Titrations

Burets are made to deliver variable amounts of liquid. During a titration, you are concerned with how much liquid has been delivered and NOT how much liquid remains in the buret. As a result, burets are read from top to bottom and subtraction is used to determine volume delivered. For example:

Volume of NaOH Soln. Delivered = Current Buret Reading - Initial Buret Reading

The buret is marked at every 0.1 mL. Read the buret to one place in between the markings, i.e., to the nearest 0.01 mL. Thus, buret readings should be given to two digits past the decimal place.

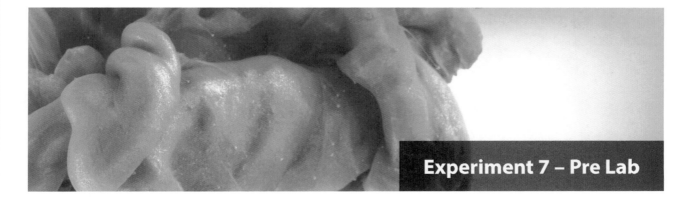

To get an idea of how titrations can be useful, consider *Figure 7-3*. Assume that 0.70 g of a drink mix powder dissolved in enough water to prepare 100 mL of solution was used to make the acidic solution and that the drink mix contains citric acid (molar mass 192 g/mol).

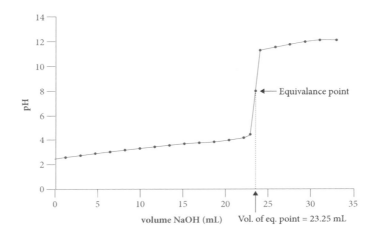

Figure 7-3: Titration curve of a citric acid solution titrated with 0.40 M NaOH.

Clearly, there is a point in the titration where the pH makes a sudden jump. To locate the exact point of equivalence, find the point of inflection, where the slope of the curve is greatest (or where the curvature changes from convex to concave). In this case, the inflection point, and equivalence, occurs after 23.25 mL of 0.40 M NaOH has been delivered.

Moles of base at the equivalence point can be determined from the volume of base delivered to reach the equivalence point and the concentration of NaOH.

1. Calculate the moles of NaOH added to reach the equivalence point (i.e., after the addition of 23.25 mL of 0.40 M NaOH).

2. Using the fact that the acid and base are in exact stoichiometric proportions at the equivalence point, calculate the *moles of citric acid* in the solution. The balanced equation is:

$$H_3C_6H_5O_7(aq) \ + \ 3\,NaOH(aq) \ \longrightarrow \ Na_3C_6H_5O_7(aq) \ + \ 3\,H_2O(l) \tag{1}$$

3. Now calculate the *mass of citric acid* in the drink mix.

4. Calculate the *mass percent citric acid* in the drink mix using Formula 2.

$$\mathbf{\%\ mass} \ = \ \frac{(\text{mass of citric acid})}{(\text{total mass of drink mix})} \ \times \ 100\%$$

As you see, from the titration data, you can determine the mass percent of acid in the drink mix. Keep these calculations handy as these same calculations will be used during the course of this experiment.

Procedure

Kool-Aid Quality Control

A. YOU WILL BE WORKING IN PAIRS FOR THIS EXPERIMENT

However, each student will turn in his/her own data report sheet. Be efficient and mindful of your time. For instance, while one partner is performing the titration, the other partner can record the data and plot the titration curve.

B. PREPARE FOR DATA COLLECTION

1. Collect approximately 100 mL of 0.7 0 M NaOH in a beaker. In *Table 7-2*, record the actual molarity of NaOH as given on the container,

2. Close the stopcock on the buret. Pour approximately 10 mL of the NaOH solution into the buret to rinse it. As shown in the prelab video, rinse all inside surfaces with the base by holding the buret at an angle and rotating. Drain the base solution through the buret tip and through the top and into a 250 mL waste beaker.

3. Fill the buret with NaOH solution to within one-half inch of the top of the buret rim. At this point, there is still air filling the buret tip. You need to remove this air by opening the stopcock until a) the solution fills the tip; b) no air bubbles remain in the tip; and c) the liquid's meniscus is level with or drops to just below the zero mark. When you close the stopcock, make sure that there are no bubbles in the tip and that the buret does not leak. If the buret leaks, ask your teaching assistant for assistance.

4. Plug in and turn on the SPARK unit. Once the SPARK software initializes, the screen will ask you to plug in a sensor. Plug the pH sensor into the top-right port of the SPARK unit. The pH probe should be resting in a soaking solution with a pH of 4.01. **Does the SPARK unit read pH ~4.01 for this soaking solution?** If so, continue on to the next step. If not, ask your teaching assistant for assistance. You may need to calibrate the pH probe before you begin. Your teaching assistant will provide instructions.

5. You will be monitoring and recording a) volume of base delivered and b) pH of the sample solution during your titration.

C. SAMPLE PREPARATION

1. Obtain a packet of Kool-Aid brand drink mix. Divide the packet of mix into four approximately equal parts. Save one portion (one-quarter of the packet) for your group and distribute the remaining portions to three other groups. Each group should weigh their quarter of the mix to obtain an accurate mass. Record this mass in *Table 7-1* of the data report sheet.

   Remember: Use the method of weighing by difference to obtain masses!

2. Dissolve your 1/4 share of mix into 200 mL distilled water. Use a graduated cylinder to measure the water volume; the scale printed on a beaker is much too inaccurate. Ensure that all of the mix dissolves by adding a stir bar and mixing the solution on the *unheated* stir plate for five minutes.

3. Use a graduated cylinder to accurately measure one-half of the drink mix solution (100 mL, one serving) into a 250 mL beaker. ***Add 4 drops phenolphthalein indicator solution***. Add a stir bar to the beaker and place it on the stir plate. (The phenolphthalein should not turn pink, since the drink mix is acidic.)

D. TITRATION

1. The pH probe should be resting in a soaking solution. Rinse the soaking solution from the pH probe by *carefully* taking the electrode from the soaking solution and placing it in 100 mL of distilled water. **NOTE: The pH electrode contains a delicate thin glass membrane and must be treated with care.** Stir **GENTLY** with the pH probe for 5 seconds to remove soaking solution from the pH electrode.

2. Place a pH probe into the drink mix solution by carefully clamping the pH probe (at the top of the probe) to a ring stand at a height such that the lower portion (sensor area) is dipped into the solution. Ensure that the probe will not be hit by the stir bar. Start the stirrer. Adjust the stir rate to produce a *gentle* vortex in the surface of the solution. **Stirring too fast will cause the stir bar to spin out of control and hit the pH probe.**

3. The tip of the NaOH-filled buret should extend a few centimeters below the mouth of the flask. You are now ready to begin your titration. You will (i) monitor the pH of the solution prior to, at, and after the equivalence point and (ii) titrate to the end point (faint pink coloration of the indicator). Be sure you have previously recorded the initial volume reading of NaOH in the buret (in *Tables 6-2 and 6-3*), as well as the concentration of the base and volume of mix solution being titrated. You can add the base in fairly large increments (in 0.50 mL increments) to the acidic mix solution until the end point is *approached*. *Monitor the pH of the solution during the titration by periodically (perhaps after every 0.5 mL added base) reading both the buret volume and solution pH and recording these values in Table 7-2*. While one partner is performing the titration, the other partner should record the data and plot the titration curve (see Step 5). As the titration progresses and the slope of the titration curve increases (at pH > 6), the incremental volume of NaOH delivered should be decreased.

   • Read the buret to one place in between the markings. (i.e., to the nearest 0.01 mL and give buret readings to two digits past the decimal place.)

4. As the end point is approached, the pink coloration will fade less quickly and the base should be added dropwise. Continue adding base until one drop causes the appearance of a faint pink color, which lasts for at least 30 seconds (the pink color gradually fades over time). Stop the titration: This is the end point. A deep pink color means that the end point has been exceeded, i.e., too much base has been added. At this end point, read the buret and record the final buret volume and solution pH in *Tables 6-2 and 6-3* (end point found from color change). In *Table 7-2*, mark the end point volume with an asterisk or "*". Continue adding base and recording pH and buret readings for ~2 mL beyond this end point to observe how the pH changes after the equivalence point.

5. Dispose of the solution in the beaker as instructed by your teaching assistant.

Procedure

Drink Mix Comparison

A. REPEAT THE TITRATION PROCEDURE, BUT USE THE GENERIC BRAND DRINK MIX.

Again, follow the procedure listed in Part C for sample preparation. Record the mass data in *Table 7-5* of the data report sheet. Follow the titration procedure outlined in Part D for titrating 100 mL of the drink mix solution EXCEPT: a) only use the indicator's color change to determine the end point; b) do not continue the titration beyond the end point; and c) go ahead and observe how the pH changes during the titration but do not write down the values or generate a titration curve. Record your results in *Table 7-6* of the data report sheet. Repeat this titration a second time with the remainder (measure and record the actual volume used) of the generic drink mix solution.

- *Be sure to use distilled water to rinse off the pH electrode before adding it to the new drink mix solution.*

- *Don't forget to add the phenolphthalein indicator!*

B. CLEAN UP

1. Drain the buret into a waste beaker. Rinse the buret with at least 20 mL of water and also let that liquid drain through the buret tip.

2. Dispose of your solutions as instructed by your teaching assistant.

3. Rinse the pH electrode with distilled water and place it back into the beaker of buffer solution. Be sure the buffer solution covers the bottom portion (~1") of the electrode. If it does not, inform your teaching assistant. Turn off the SPARK and unplug the SPARK sensors, and unplug the stir plate.

C. CALCULATIONS AND ANALYSIS

1. On the graph paper with the Experiment 7 data report sheet, generate a titration curve by making a plot of pH (y-axis) vs. Volume of NaOH Delivered (x-axis).

   - Be sure to use as much of the graph paper as possible because data obtained from a large plot is more accurate than data obtained from a small plot.

   - Label both the x- and y-axes with titles and units.

   - Give your graph a title e.g., Kool-Aid Titration Curve: Solution pH vs. Volume of NaOH Delivered.

2. From the inflection point of the titration curve (see prelab), determine the volume of base delivered to reach the equivalence point. Draw a vertical line from the inflection point to the corresponding volume. Record this volume in *Table 7-3* (under equivalence point found from pH). Complete the rest of the calculations in *Table 7-3*. Pool your percent citric acid results with three groups from other rows who used the same Kool-Aid mix (brand and type). Record these values in *Table 7-4* and based on these four values calculate an average percent citric acid value for the Kool-Aid.

3. Double-check all of your calculations and significant figures. Include units on all of your numbers. Have your teaching assistant verify by signing your completion of this experiment. Rip off and hand in the data report sheets (pages 79-81) for grading. Each student is to turn in his/her own data report sheet. However, students working in pairs should include their partner's name on the data report sheet. Dispose of all chemical wastes as indicated by your teaching assistant.

CALCULATIONS:

Show your calculations below. Watch your units and report all answers with the correct number of significant figures.

Data

Table 7.1: Kool-Aid Sample: Data

Kool-Aid Sample Type	Mass of Mix in Your 1/4 Packet (g)	Volume 1/4 Packet Mix Was Diluted to (mL)
lemonade or invisible		

Table 7.2: Kool-Aid Sample: pH vs. Volume of Base Data

Volume of Kool-Aid Mix Solution Titrated	Mass of Mix in Volume Titrated	Molarity of NaOH Solution Used

Buret Reading (mL)	Volume (in mL) NaOH Delivered*	Solution pH	Buret Reading (mL)	Volume (in mL) NaOH Delivered*	Solution pH

Remember: Volume (in mL) of NaOH delivered = Current Buret Reading at each point – Initial Buret Reading

Table 7-2. *Continued*

Buret Reading (mL)	Volume (in mL) NaOH Delivered*	Solution pH	Buret Reading (mL)	Volume (in mL) NaOH Delivered*	Solution pH

** **Remember:** Volume (in mL) of NaOH delivered = Current Buret Reading at each point – Initial Buret Reading*

Table 7-3. Kool-Aid Sample: Calculations

Kool-Aid Sample Type	Volume of Kool-Aid Mix Solution Titrated	Mass of Mix in Volume Titrated	Molarity of NaOH Solution Used
lemonade or invisible			

Calculations	Equivalence Point Found by pH	End Point Found by Color Change
buret reading at end point	NA	
initial buret reading	NA	
volume of NaOH delivered to reach eq point or end point		
moles of NaOH		
moles of citric acid		
mass of citric acid in volume of Kool-Aid titrated		
% citric acid in drink mix		

Table 7-4. Comparison of Kool-Aid Values

	Your Row	Other Row 1	Other Row 2	Other Row 3
student lab drawer numbers				
% citric acid in Kool-Aid Brand				

Based on these four data points, what is the average percent citric acid in the Kool-Aid mix you used? _____ %

How do your values compare with the other three sets of students? Are they close? Does the Kool-Aid mix have good quality control in terms of percent citric acid in the packet?

Did the end and equivalence points in your titration give the same results in terms of percent citric acid in the drink mix? Which do you think is more accurate for signifying the stopping point in a titration, the end point or the equivalence point? Explain.

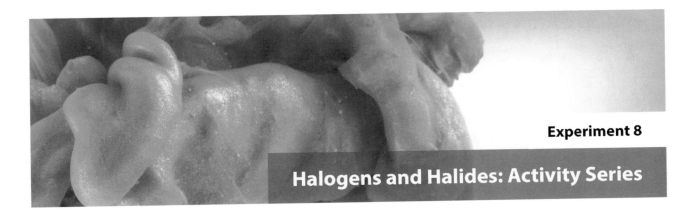

Halogens and Halides: Activity Series

Materials List

- concentrated H_2SO_4 (sulfuric acid)
- 0.10 M $AgNO_3$ (silver nitrate)
- 6.00 M $Ca(NO_3)_2 \cdot 4H_2O$ (calcium nitrate tetrahydrate)
- Cl_2 water

- Br_2 water
- NaBr (sodium bromide)
- NaCl (sodium chloride)
- NaF (sodium fluoride)
- NaI (sodium iodide)

Objectives

After completing this project, you will be able to:

- identify halogens using precipitation and redox reactions.
- apply knowledge of the non-metal activity series to determine if a reaction between non-metals will occur.
- balance redox reactions involving halogens.
- predict products and write net ionic equations involving halogens and halides.

Introduction

Properties of the Halogens

The non-metal elements in Group VIIA (F, Cl, Br, I, and At), referred to as the halogens, are generally symbolized by an X. Under standard conditions, the halogens exist as diatomic molecules, X_2. Each halogen has seven valence electrons and a valence electronic configuration ns^2np^5. During reactions, and in order to satisfy the octet rule, each halogen (X) tends to gain one electron to be *reduced* (meaning to gain electrons) to X^-. The anion X^- (*or halide ion*) has a valence electronic configuration ns^2np^6, which satisfies the octet rule. This experiment is designed to give you a feel for the properties of the halogens (excluding astatine) and of some of their simple precipitation and redox reactions. A series of reactions will be performed, first, on the known halide compounds of NaF, NaCl, NaBr, and NaI. Detailed observations of precipitates formed, colors, color changes, odors, etc., should be recorded. The same reactions will be performed on an unknown, which contains one of the halide ions. The following physical properties of the halogens and other chemicals will help in interpreting the results of this experiment:

1. **Chlorine:** $Cl_2(g)$ is faint yellowish-green in color. In a small test tube, this gas may be almost invisible. Chlorine, $Cl_2(aq)$, is nearly colorless to pale green, depending on the concentration.

2. **Bromine:** $Br_2(g)$ and $Br_2(l)$ are red in color. $Br_2(aq)$ is faint yellowish-red in color, depending on the concentration.

3. **Iodine:** $I_2(g)$ is violet in color. Iodine, $I_2(s)$, is nearly black in color. Iodine, $I_2(aq)$, is faint yellow. However, I_2 is only slightly soluble in water; therefore, it may be present as a dark-colored, suspended solid whenever formed from an aqueous solution.

4. **Hydrogen Halides (HX):** Gaseous HF, HCl, HBr, and HI are all colorless and their aqueous solutions are colorless as well. Blowing your hot breath across the mouth of a test tube in which one of these gases is produced will result in the formation of a white fog.

5. Chlorine, Cl_2, and bromine, Br_2, and their solutions will bleach moist litmus paper white because of their strong oxidizing capabilities.

6. Sulfur dioxide, $SO_2(g)$, has the odor of burning sulfur (the odor of a freshly struck and flaming match head). Hydrogen sulfide, $H_2S(g)$, has the odor of rotten eggs.

Scientific Background

Halogen Non-Metal Activity Series

In compounds, the halogens tend to be found in the reduced form (i.e., as F^-, Cl^-, Br^-, and I^-). However, each halogen (X_2) has a different tendency to be reduced. Of the halogens, fluorine (F_2) is the most readily reduced and is therefore the strongest oxidizing agent. Whereas, iodine (I_2) is the least readily reduced and is therefore the weakest oxidizing agent. A list of the halogens in order of decreasing ability as oxidizing agents is shown in (1). This list is referred to as the non-metal activity series.

Strongest   Weakest

Oxidizing Agent   →→→   Oxidizing Agent

$$F_2 \quad > \quad Cl_2 \quad > \quad Br_2 \quad > \quad I_2 \tag{1}$$

The non-metal activity series can be used to predict whether a redox reaction between two halogens will occur spontaneously in the forward direction. For example, consider the redox reaction shown in (2). This reaction will proceed spontaneously in the forward direction because

$$2\ Br^- + F_2 \longrightarrow 2\ F^- + Br_2 \tag{2}$$

fluorine is a better oxidizing agent than bromine (i.e., $F_2 > Br_2$ in the non-metal activity series). This indicates that fluorine wants to be in the reduced form (as F^-) more than bromine and so will act to get in that form. As a result, F_2 will spontaneously reduce to F^-, while, Br^- will spontaneously oxidize to Br_2. As a second example, consider the reaction shown in (3). This reaction will not proceed spontaneously in the forward direction because chlorine is a better oxidizing agent than bromine

$$2\ Cl^- + Br_2 \longrightarrow \text{No Reaction} \tag{3}$$

(i.e., $Cl_2 > Br_2$ in the non-metal activity series). This indicates that chlorine wants to be in the reduced form (as Cl^-) more than bromine and so will act to get or stay in that form. In reaction (3), the chlorine reactant is already in the reduced form and so no reaction will occur spontaneously in the forward direction.

Procedure

Part I: Precipitation Reactions and Simple Redox Reactions of the Halides

All students are to work individually on all parts of this experiment. However, you are welcome to compare and contrast your experimental results and share chemicals (properly labeled) with your neighbor. As you complete the experiment, record all of your experimental data (observations/product chemical formulas) in Tables 8-1 and 8-2.

1. **Tests on NaI:** In a small test tube, place a small quantity (about the size of a large pea) of solid NaI. Add 4 mL of distilled water and stir until all of the solid is dissolved. Use ~1 mL of this solution for each of the following tests.

   a. **AgNO$_3$ Test:** To ~1 mL of the NaI solution add five drops of AgNO$_3$(aq). Stir. Note whether a precipitate forms and any associated color changes. Record your observations in Table 8-1.

   b. **Ca(NO$_3$)$_2$ Test:** To ~1 mL of the NaI solution add 10 drops of Ca(NO$_3$)$_2$(aq). Stir. Note whether a precipitate forms and any associated color changes. Record your observations in Table 8-1.

   c. **Cl$_2$ Test:** To ~1 mL of the NaI solution add ~1 mL of Cl$_2$ water. **NOTE: Before using the Cl$_2$ water, be certain it contains a greenish color indicative of dissolved Cl$_2$. This solution rapidly loses Cl$_2$ in a warm laboratory.** Stir. Note any color changes and any precipitate formation. Record your observations in Table 8-1.

   d. **Br$_2$ Test:** To ~1 mL of the NaI solution add ~1 mL of Br$_2$ water. Stir. Note any color changes and any precipitate formation. Record your observations in Table 8-1.

2. **Tests on NaBr:** In a small test tube, place a small quantity (about the size of a large pea) of solid NaBr. Add 4 mL of distilled water and stir until all of the solid is dissolved. As for the NaI solution in Step 1, use ~1 mL of this NaBr solution for *each* of the tests in a, b, and c. Record your observations in Table 8-1.

3. **Tests on NaCl:** In a small test tube, place a small quantity (about the size of a large pea) of solid NaCl. Add 4 mL of distilled water and stir until all of the solid is dissolved. As for the NaI solution in Step 1, use ~1 mL of this NaCl solution for ***each*** of the tests in a and b. Record your observations in Table 8-1.

4. **Tests on NaF:** In a small test tube, place a small quantity (about the size of a large pea) of solid NaF. Add 4 mL of distilled water and stir until all of the solid is dissolved. As for the NaI solution in Step 1, use ~1 mL of this NaF solution for ***each*** of the tests in a and b. Record your observations in Table 8-1.

Table 8.1: Part I: Experimental Observations (Part I).

Tests On	$AgNO_3$(aq)	$Ca(NO_3)_2$(aq)	Cl_2 Water	Br_2 Water
NaI				
NaBr				
NaCl				
NaF				
Unknown				

Part II: Reaction of the Halides with Sulfuric Acid

1. **Ask the Teaching Assistant to dispense the concentrated H_2SO_4 for you.**

CAUTION: Concentrated H_2SO_4 is corrosive. Immediately wash spills with lots of water and inform your Teaching Assistant. Use a small, clean, dry beaker to obtain a minimal amount (~2 mL) of concentrated H_2SO_4. Share this chemical with a neighbor.

2. **NaF and H_2SO_4:** In a small test tube, place a small quantity (about the size of a pea) of solid NaF. Use a medicine dropper to add five drops of concentrated sulfuric acid. **CAUTION: Add H_2SO_4 one drop at a time while holding the test tube with test tube holders under the *student hood*.** Make the following observations and record in Table 8-2:

   a. Is a gas evolved? If so, what is the color of the gas? What is the color of the solution?

   b. With hot breath, ***carefully blow across*** (do not inhale the fumes!) the mouth of the test tube. Does a white fog result?

   c. Test the acidity of the escaping gas (not the sides of the test tube) with moist blue litmus.[1] Does the litmus paper change color?

   d. Discard the contents of the test tube. Rinse the tube with copious amounts of water. Examine the bottom of the test tube for possible chemical *etching*.[2] Was chemical etching apparent?

3. **NaCl and H_2SO_4:** Repeat the experiment in Step 2, above, except use NaCl.

4. **NaBr and H_2SO_4:** Repeat the experiment in Step 2, above, except use NaBr. Also, ***very cautiously*** use your hand to direct some of the gas evolved toward your nose. You should be able to detect the odor of burning sulfur, due to SO_2, beyond the stench of bromine.

5. **NaI and H_2SO_4:** Repeat the experiment in Step 2, above, except use NaI. Also, ***very cautiously*** use your hand to direct some of the gas evolved toward your nose. You should be able to detect the odor of rotten eggs due to evolution of H_2S.

6. The laboratory Teaching Assistant must approve your observations in Tables 8-1 and 8-2.

Teaching Assistant's Approval:

_____

Signature

---

1 Litmus paper contains an indicator that is used to test the relative acidity of a substance or solution. The acidic color of litmus paper is red, whereas the basic color of litmus paper is blue.

2 Etching involves the chemical reaction between glass, which is relatively chemically resistant, and another substance. Glass that has been etched appears cloudy and/or highly scratched.

Table 8.2: Part II: Experimental Observations.

Tests On	NaF	NaCl	NaBr	NaI	Unknown
Gas? Color?					
White Fog?					
Litmus?					
Etching?					
Odor?					

Procedure

Part III: Unknown (Contains One of the Following Ions: F⁻, Cl⁻, Br⁻, or I⁻)

1. On the unknown, perform ALL of the tests outlined in Parts I and II. By comparison with your earlier observations, decide which halide ion is present in your unknown. Fill in the Data Report Sheet for Experiment 7 and have your Teaching Assistant verify your completion of this experiment by signing. Rip off and hand in the Data Report Sheet for grading. Dispose of all chemical wastes as indicated by your Teaching Assistant.

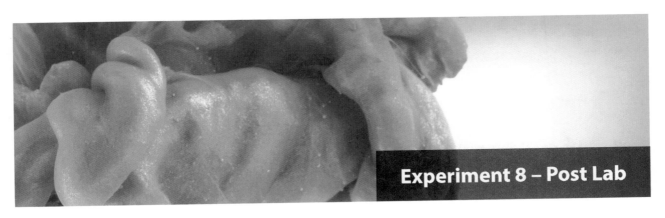

1. The following reactions were carried out in Part I of this experiment. For each, predict products, write a balanced net ionic equation, and give colors or other evidence of reaction written beneath the net ionic equation. Show all work, including balanced molecular equation and intermediate full ionic equation.

    a. $NaI(aq) + AgNO_3(aq) \longrightarrow$

        Net Ionic Equation:

    b. $NaI(aq) + Ca(NO_3)_2(aq) \longrightarrow$

        Net Ionic Equation:

    c. $NaI(aq) + Cl_2(aq) \longrightarrow$

        Net Ionic Equation:

    d. $NaI(aq) + Br_2(aq) \longrightarrow$

        Net Ionic Equation:

    e. $NaBr(aq) + AgNO_3(aq) \longrightarrow$

        Net Ionic Equation:

    f. $NaBr(aq) + Ca(NO_3)_2(aq) \longrightarrow$

        Net Ionic Equation:

    g. $NaBr(aq) + Cl_2(aq) \longrightarrow$

        Net Ionic Equation:

h. $NaCl(aq) + AgNO_3(aq) \longrightarrow$

      Net Ionic Equation:

i. $NaCl(aq) + Ca(NO_3)_2(aq) \longrightarrow$

      Net Ionic Equation:

j. $NaF(aq) + AgNO_3(aq) \longrightarrow$

      Net Ionic Equation:

k. $NaF(aq) + Ca(NO_3)_2(aq) \longrightarrow$

      Net Ionic Equation:

2. Why were no tests made for the blanks blacked out in Table 8-1? (Hint: Use your knowledge of the non-metal activity series.)

3. In which two ways could you be certain whether or not a solution contained the fluoride ion? NOTE: Presence or absence of etching is not conclusive evidence for or against fluoride ion presence.

4. Could you distinguish between the chloride, bromide, and iodide ions solely on the basis of the results from the silver nitrate test? Explain your answer. Why is this not the best way to distinguish between these ions?

5. The following reactions were carried out in Part II of this experiment. For each, predict products and write a balanced net ionic equation. Show all work, including balanced molecular equation and intermediate full ionic equation.

   a. $NaF(aq) + H_2SO_4(aq) \longrightarrow$

Net Ionic Equation:

   b. $NaCl(aq) + H_2SO_4(aq) \longrightarrow$

      Net Ionic Equation:

6. The following reactions were carried out in Part II of this experiment. The reactions of NaBr and NaI with concentrated H_2SO_4 occur as redox reactions. The unbalanced reactions are shown below. For each, balance the redox reaction and write a balanced net ionic equation. Show all work (e.g., balanced half-reactions, oxidation numbers, etc.) used to balance the molecular equation and all work used to obtain the net ionic equation.

   a. $NaBr(aq) + H_2SO_4(aq) \longrightarrow Br_2(l) + SO_2(g) + H_2O(l) + Na_2SO_4(aq)$

      Balanced Redox Reaction:

      Net Ionic Equation:

   b. $NaI(aq) + H_2SO_4(aq) \longrightarrow I_2(aq) + H_2S(g) + H_2O(l) + Na_2SO_4(aq)$

      Balanced Redox Reaction:

      Net Ionic Equation:

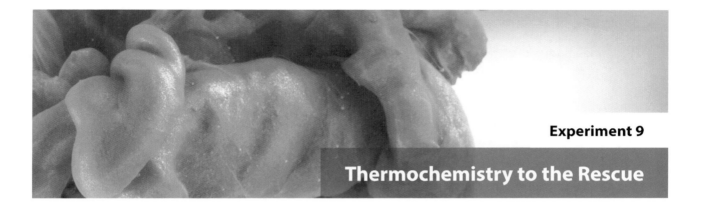

Thermochemistry to the Rescue

- Chemical splash goggles, gloves, and apron must be worn at all times.
- Tie back long hair and loose sleeves.

Materials List

- Sodium chloride, NaCl (CAS registry number 7647-14-5)
- Potassium chloride, KCl (CAS registry number 7447-40-7)
- Anhydrous calcium chloride, $CaCl_2$ (CAS registry number 10043-52-4)
- Vienna sausages (purchase at local grocery store)

Objectives

- After completing this project, you will be able to:
- Identify a reaction as exothermic or endothermic from the sign of ΔH or ΔT.
- Convert between ΔH and q.
- Convert between a change in temperature, ΔH for a reaction, and specific heat.
- Use scientific process skills (e.g., observing, measuring, inferring, and predicting) to problem solve a solution for a simulated real-world situation.
- Relate chemistry content to real-world applications.

Introduction

The human body works best within a very narrow temperature range. A temperature drop of as little as 2 °C in the body's core causes classic hypothermia symptoms such as mental difficulties and loss of physical coordination. Much more extreme temperature drops in the extremities may be survived, but can lead to frostnip or frostbite if the flesh freezes. Victims of hypothermia require immediate treatment, and in outdoor situations the treatment is often warmth provided by portable heat sources, such as heat packs.

Heat packs that produce warmth through various chemical reactions are available. Such heat packs are convenient because they only release heat when triggered. One common heat pack contains an internal pouch of water and a solid powder. Once the pouch of water is broken open, there is an exothermic reaction between the water and the powder. These heat packs have limitations. For example, they do not work well in extreme cold; the water will freeze.

In the coldest environments, heat packs are available that contain only the powder in a resealable waterproof sack. When heat is needed, the sack can be opened and any aqueous solution poured inside. The sack is resealed and the reaction produces heat. Any aqueous solution will work: melted snow, stream water, coffee, even urine.

As part of this lab, you will:

- Measure the amount of heat involved in frostbite.
- Examine a possible heat-generating reaction for a heat pack.
- Use your results to design a heat pack for treating human frostbite.

Scientific Background

Reaction Enthalpy

An important part of modern chemistry involves studying energy changes that occur during chemical reactions. These energy changes are of fundamental importance in understanding the "driving force" of a chemical reaction. The most common way energy is exchanged between a chemical system and the environment is by evolution or absorption of *heat* (q). The change in heat energy accompanying a chemical reaction is known as *enthalpy change*, ΔH. By convention, reactions in which *heat is absorbed* are labeled *endothermic* and have *positive values* of ΔH; reactions in which *heat is released* are labeled *exothermic* and have *negative values* of ΔH. Cold packs used in athletics are familiar to many sports enthusiasts. In order to derive coldness from the pack, a plastic packet of water is broken inside another packet containing a solid salt such as NH_4NO_3. In this case, the enthalpy of solution, i.e., heat absorbed or released when a substance dissolves, is endothermic, indicating that heat is absorbed as the salt dissolves. Thus, the enthalpy of solution is designated with a positive sign.

$$NH_4NO_3(s) \longrightarrow NH_4NO_3(aq) \qquad \Delta H = +25.7 \text{ kJ}$$

Gas stoves often produce heat through the combustion (burning in oxygen) of methane (equation 1). Since heat is produced by the combustion, the reaction is exothermic and *enthalpy of combustion* (ΔH), i.e., heat released during combustion, must be negative. In fact, ΔH for the methane combustion in (1) is 890.4 kJ. It is important to realize that ΔH is related to the coefficients in the balanced equation. Thus, -890.4 kJ of heat is released per every 1 mole of CH_4 that reacts but per every two moles of H_2O that is formed.

$$CH_4(g) + 2 O_2(g) \longrightarrow CO_2(g) + 2 H_2O(g) \qquad \Delta H = 2890.4 \text{ kJ} \qquad (1)$$

The amount of heat (q) absorbed or released by any reaction is calculated by equation 2.

$$q = (\text{\# of mol of chemical}) \times \frac{\Delta H}{\text{chemical's coefficient}} \qquad (2)$$

For instance, the amount of heat (q) produced by the combustion of 2.0 mol methane in an excess of oxygen would be:

$$2.0 \text{ mol } CH_4 \times \frac{-890.4 \text{ kj}}{1 \text{ mol } CH_4} = -1780.8 \text{ kj} \longrightarrow -1.8 \times 10^3 \text{ kj}$$

Here the negative is redundant since the original statement mentioned that heat was produced. However, the negative sign serves to reinforce the fact of heat production rather than absorption.

Heat and Temperature

If an object (such as a pot of water) is positioned to absorb the heat given off during a combustion reaction, then the temperature of the object will change. Equation 3 governs the temperature change

$$q = m \times c \times \Delta T \qquad (3)$$

where

q = the amount of heat absorbed by the object

m = the mass of the object being heated

c = the specific heat of the object being heated

ΔT = the change in temperature of the object = $T_f - T_i$

The specific heat is different for different substances. For example,

Substance	Specific Heat $(J \cdot g^{-1} {}^\circ C^{-1})$
Water	4.18
Air	1.01
Aluminum	0.897
Granite	0.790

Calorimetry

Many experiments in thermochemistry involve a calorimeter. A calorimeter is simply a container that insulates a reaction from the surrounding environment. Usually, a calorimeter will have a water bath that changes temperature, up or down, depending on whether the reaction is exothermic or endothermic. For many aqueous reactions, the water bath is the solution itself, as in today's lab. Your calorimeter will be a simple nested polystyrene cup arrangement (i.e., coffee cup calorimeter). Polystyrene is an excellent insulator, but with time heat will slowly leak out of the cup. By plotting temperature of the solution versus time, you will be able to distinguish between the temperature changes due to a reaction and the temperature changes due to heat leaking through the insulator.

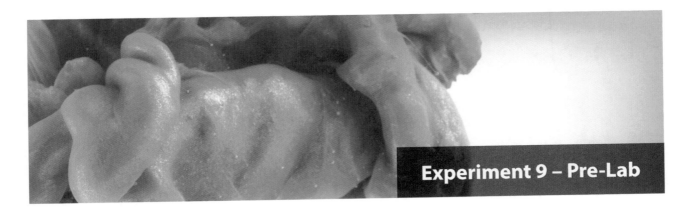

Stovetop Thermochemistry

Calculate the amount of heat, q, produced by the combustion of 4.05 g CH_4 (ΔH_{comb} = 2890.4 kJ). See the calculation shown on page 95 for help with this calculation.

Consider that the 4.05 g methane is burned and all of the heat lost from this combustion (heat lost) is absorbed (heat gained) by 1.0 kg of 20 °C water (ignore the pot holding the water, and use 4.18 $J \cdot g^{-1}$ $°C^{-1}$ for the specific heat of the water). What would be the final temperature of the water? Solve by following the steps below.

First, rearrange equation 3 to solve for ΔT. Show your rearrangement of equation 3 below.

Now, plug into your equation the values for q, m, and c to find ΔT (be mindful of your kJ and J units).

Finally, knowing ΔT and the initial temperature, T_i, find the final temperature, T_f, of the water.

Procedure

Part I: Frostbite—Approximation of Specific Heat of Human Hand

What's the Point of Measuring a Specific Heat?

Obviously, heat must be taken from a person's hand to cool it down, and heat must be added to warm it up again. But how *much heat* (*taken or added*) is governed by the hand's *specific heat*. Specific heat is the amount of heat required to increase the temperature of 1 g of a substance by 1^0C. To know how much heat is involved, you will need first to estimate the specific heat of the human hand.

A. INSTRUCTIONS

1. As you complete the experiment, record all data within the data tables on the Experiment 9 Data Report Sheet. Include all of your calculations on pages 103-104. Work in pairs on all parts of this experiment and be efficient and mindful of your time. However, each student will turn in his/her own Data Report Sheets.

B. SETUP

1. Create an ice slush in a 250-mL beaker. Fill the beaker with ice and add just enough water to produce a slush. The goal *IS NOT* to make ice water, but to make packed ice with water between the pieces of ice. The temperature of an ice slush is the melting/freezing temperature of water.

2. Obtain one Vienna sausage and press it into the ice slush. Notice the sausage's eerie similarity to a section of a human finger. You will take advantage of this similarity today. The sausage (and other meat products) will have a specific heat close to that of a finger and/or the human hand. ***Do not taste the sausages! Food items brought into a chemistry laboratory are no longer safe to eat.***

3. If the ice slush melts into ice water during the experiment, pour off some water and refill with ice to recreate the slush.

4. Plug in and turn on the PASCO SPARK unit.

5. Once the SPARK software initializes, the screen will ask you to plug in a sensor. Plug the temperature sensor into the top of the unit.

6. From the options that appear on the screen, choose "Temperature" and press "Show."

7. A graph will appear. The SPARK is now ready to collect data.

C. MEASURE THE SPECIFIC HEAT OF FLESH

1. Obtain a coffee cup calorimeter (two nested polystyrene cups). Add 100-mL tap water to the calorimeter. Cover the cup with the cardboard provided, and insert a glass rod and the temperature probe through the hole in the cardboard. **CAUTION: Be careful not to poke a hole in the coffee cup with the temperature probe. This could invalidate your results.**

2. Press the green ▶ button on the SPARK to begin data collection. Collect data for at least 700 seconds (or ~12 minutes). After one minute, lift the cardboard and quickly transfer one sausage from the ice slush into the calorimeter. Note the time at which the sausage was added. Be sure to quickly shake any ice pieces from the sausage before putting it into the calorimeter. Replace the cardboard and gently stir the solution continuously with the glass rod.

3. The temperature should drop and reach a plateau, where it remains constant for at least 15 seconds. After the plateau, the temperature will probably rise slowly as heat leaks in from the surroundings. To better observe the temperature changes, you should autoscale the graph. First, press the graph options button at the bottom-left corner of the graph, and then autoscale the plot by pressing the top-right graph options button (the expand button). You should be able to clearly see the flat region before adding the sausage to the water, and the drop in temperature to the plateau.

4. Press the red ▶ button on the unit to stop data collection (after at least 700 seconds).

5. Remove the sausage from the water, dry it off, and weigh it. Record this value on the Data Report Sheet Part 1 in Table 9-1.

6. Examine the graph to locate the initial flat portion of the graph and the plateau at lower temperatures.

7. Press the top-left graph option (the arrow button) and a point on the plot within the flat initial region. Find the time of sausage addition within this initial flat region and extrapolate this back to the temperature axis to determine the temperature at this point. This is the initial temperature, T_i, of the water at the time of sausage addition. Record this value on the Data Report Sheet Part 1 in Table 9-1. Turn off the arrow button.

8. Similarly determine the final temperature, T_f, from the plateau region by extrapolation of the plateau region after addition back to the temperature axis. Fill in the rest of Table 9-1 in the Data Report Sheet Part 1. Use equation 3 to determine the amount of heat lost from the water as its temperature dropped.

9. Since the calorimeter was insulating, the amount of heat that was lost by the water must have been gained by the sausage to raise its temperature. As a result, within the calorimeter

Heat (q) gained by the sausage = −Heat (q) lost by the water

This simple statement, "*heat gained = −heat lost*", forms the basis for all calorimetry calculations.

10. The final temperature of the sausage should be the same as the final temperature of the water. What was the initial temperature of the sausage?

11. Again using equation 3 for the sausage, solve for the specific heat of the sausage to fill in the last line in Table 9-1.

Part II: Portable Heat Pack Thermodynamics

D. EXOTHERMIC AND ENDOTHERMIC DISSOLUTION

1. In this section of the procedure, you will observe temperature changes as various salts are dissolved in water. The first salt is NaCl, and the corresponding dissolution reaction is shown in (4).

$$NaCl(s) \xrightarrow{H_2O} Na^+(aq) + Cl^-(aq) \qquad\qquad (4)$$

2. Insert the end of the temperature probe into the bottom of a test tube. Fill the test tube approximately 2 cm with distilled water. Fill a second test tube approximately 1 cm with NaCl. Start data collection by pressing the green ▶ button on the SPARK. Move to Page 2 of the display (top-left of screen) to switch to the numeric temperature display.

3. After collecting data for 30 seconds, pour NaCl into the water and stir gently with a glass rod. Monitor the temperature on the SPARK screen. Record your observations in Table 9-2 of the Data Report Sheet.

4. Repeat the above procedure, but use KCl in place of NaCl. Record your observations in Table 9-2 of the Data Report Sheet.

5. Write the dissolution reaction of KCl in water.

6. Repeat the above procedure, but use $CaCl_2$ in place of NaCl. Record your observations in Table 9-2 of the Data Report Sheet.

7. Write the dissolution reaction of $CaCl_2$ in water.

8. Remove the data from the SPARK. Open the Tools menu, choose "Manage Runs," and select "Delete all Runs."

9. Which salt would work best to fashion a heat pack? Why?

Have your Teaching Assistant approve Parts I and II by signing below before moving on to the next phase in the procedure.

Teaching Assistant's Approval:

_____

Signature

E. MEASURE THE HEAT PRODUCED BY $CaCl_2$ DISSOLUTION

1. Add 100 mL tap water to the coffee cup calorimeter and place the temperature probe in the water at the bottom of the cup. Cover the calorimeter with the cardboard provided and insert a glass rod through the hole in the cardboard.

2. Using the method of weighing by difference, precisely weigh (use the electronic balance) between 8–12 g $CaCl_2$. Record the mass in Table 9-3.

3. Start data collection. After one minute, lift the cardboard and pour in the $CaCl_2$. Record the time of $CaCl_2$ addition. Replace the cardboard and gently stir the solution continuously with the glass rod. The temperature should hit a peak and then reach a plateau, where it remains constant for at least 15 seconds. After the plateau, the temperature will drop as heat is lost to the surroundings. Once the plateau has been reached and the temperature drops, you may stop data collection.

4. Examine the graph as you did before, and fill in Table 9-3 in the Data Report Sheet. Determine the initial temperature of the solution, T_i, by extrapolation of the time of $CaCl_2$ addition within the initial plateau region back to the temperature axis. Determine the final temperature, T_f, by extrapolation of the final plateau region back to the temperature axis.

5. In your calculations, you can assume that the heat absorbed by the solution to raise its temperature is equal to the amount of heat generated by the reaction. Also, assume that the specific heat of the solution is the same as that of pure water, 4.18 $J \cdot g^{-1} \, ^\circ C^{-1}$.

6. Repeat the procedure two more times. For the second sample, use 70 mL tap water. For the third sample, use 50 mL tap water. You should use approximately the same mass of $CaCl_2$ each time.

Part III: Development of a Heat Pack

Your goal for this part of today's lab is to design a heat pack for maintenance workers on the Alaskan pipeline. Your heat pack must be able to treat frostbite in a worker's hand. Consider that the hand has been cooled from normal body temperature of 37 °C down to a dangerous 15 °C, at profound risk of frostbite. How much $CaCl_2$ should be in the heat pack, and how much water should be added to activate it? Record all of your data within Table 9-4. Show all of your calculations on pages 103-104.

1. Estimate the volume of your hand in units of sausages. In other words, how many sausages would have the same volume as your hand? From this number, estimate the mass of your hand (assuming it to be equal to the mass of an equivalent volume of sausage).

2. Calculate how much heat would be required to raise the temperature of your hand from 15 °C to 37 °C, assuming that your hand has the same specific heat as the sausage (use your value from Table 9-1).

3. Calculate the amount of $CaCl_2$ that would be needed to produce this amount of heat. Hint: Use one of your ΔH_{rxn} ($J \cdot g^{-1}$ $CaCl_2$) values from Table 9-3.

4. Look back on Table 9-3 of the Data Report Sheet. The heat pack should ideally produce temperatures between 37 °C and 40 °C from an initial temperature of 15 °C (thus temperature changes of 22–25 °C). Estimate the mass ratio of $CaCl_2$: water that would produce a temperature change in this range.

5. Propose a heat pack recipe in Table 9-5 of the Data Report Sheet.

6. Test your heat pack formulation! Create a heat pack in a sealable plastic bag according to your calculations and test its performance (by measuring initial and final temperatures!).

7. Double-check all of your calculations and significant figures. Include units on all of your numbers. Have your Teaching Assistant verify your completion of this experiment by signing. Rip off and hand in the Data Report Sheets (pages 120-121) for grading. Each student is to turn in his/her own Data Report Sheet. However, students working in pairs should include their partner's name on the Data Report Sheet. Dispose of all chemical wastes as indicated by your Teaching Assistant.

Calculations: Show your calculations below. Watch your units and report all answers with the correct number of significant figures.

Calculations: Show your calculations below. Watch your units and report all answers with the correct number of significant figures.

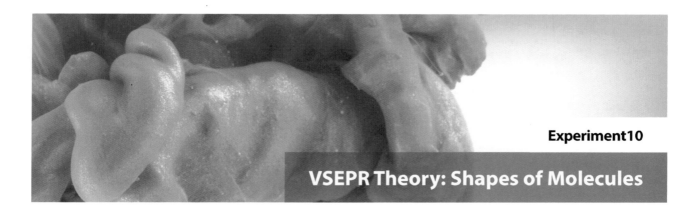

VSEPR Theory: Shapes of Molecules

SAFETY PRECAUTIONS

- As long as drawers are not opened during this laboratory session, chemical splash goggles and apron are not required.

Objectives

After completing this project, you will be able to:

- Draw Lewis structures of covalent/molecular compounds and ions.
- Build three-dimensional models.
- Predict molecular shape and bond angles.
- Predict molecular polarity.

Introduction

It is important to realize that most molecules and ions extend their shapes (arrangement of atoms) in all three dimensions. This three-dimensional shape governs physical properties such as solubility in water, boiling point temperature, vapor pressure, and chemical properties (i.e., ability to react) in biological reactions. Two examples of the importance of three-dimensional (3-D) shape are discussed below.

Example 1: *cis*-platin

In 1978, the drug *cis*-platin, *cis*-$Pt(NH_3)_2Cl_2$ or *cis*-diamminedichloroplatinum(II), gained approval from the Federal Drug Administration (FDA) for use as an anti-cancer drug in chemotherapy treatments. However, *trans*-platin, *trans*-$Pt(NH_3)_2Cl_2$ or *trans*-diamminedichloroplatinum(II), a chemical with the **same** chemical formula, does not exhibit comparable anti-cancer fighting properties and was not approved for use in chemotherapy treatments.[1] Why not? Even though the two forms of platin (*cis* and *trans*) have the same chemical formula, their 3-D shapes are markedly

1 Smith, A. Cisplatin: The invention of an anticancer drug. http://www.chemcases.com/cisplat/ (accessed Sept. 16, 2009).

different (see Figure 10-1). In *cis*-platin, the two chlorine atoms are situated 90° apart, whereas in *trans*-platin, the two chlorine atoms are situated 180° apart. This small difference in the 3-D arrangement of atoms in space corresponds to a large difference in anti-cancer fighting properties (i.e., chemical reactivity).

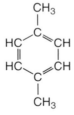

cis-platin
anti-cancer drug

trans-platin
not active as an
anti-cancer drug

Figure 10-1: Three-dimensional structures of *cis*- and *trans*-platin.

Example 2: Sense of Smell

The act of smelling an odor, *olfaction*, is highly dependent on the 3-D shape of the molecules in an airborne substance. The human olfactory system detects an odor when an airborne molecule of the correct size and three-dimensional shape fits into a corresponding cavity in an olfactory receptor cell within the nose. Odor detection is similar to a lock and key mechanism where the airborne odor molecule is the key and the cavity in the receptor cell is the lock. Only airborne molecules (keys) of the correct size and shape will be able to fit into receptor cavities (locks) to trigger (unlock) nerve cell responses and odor detection.[2,3] Research has shown that there are seven basic odors (musky, camphoric, ethereal, pepperminty, floral, pungent, and putrid) that are differentiated primarily by their 3-D molecular shape. For instance, molecules that exhibit musky odors are disk-shaped, while molecules that exhibit pepperminty odors are wedge-shaped. Each odor is associated with one of seven different types of receptor cells that can detect a small number of molecules of related 3-D shape as odor.

Space Filling Model of Xylene[4]

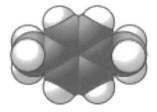

Lewis Structure of Xylene

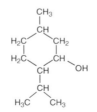

Xylene (C_8H_{10})

- Chemical responsible for *musky odor* of aftershave
- This molecule is relatively flat in the third dimension and is **disk-shaped**

Space Filling Model of Menthol[5]

Lewis Structure of Menthol

Menthol ($C_{10}H_{20}O$)

- Chemical responsible for *peppermint odor* of gum and candy
- This molecule is not flat and is *wedge-shaped* (like a piece of pie)

---

2 Bauer, R.C., Birk, J.P., and Marks, P.S. 2007. A Conceptual Introduction to Chemistry, 301–302. Boston, MA: McGraw Hill.

3 Dowdy, S. 2007. How Smell Works at How Stuff Works.com. http://health.howstuffworks.com/smell.htm (accessed Sept. 16, 2009).

4 Space filling model for xylene was obtained from Wikepedia Commons Public Domain at http://commons.wikimedia.org/wiki/File:P-xylene-spaceFilling.png (accessed Sept. 16, 2009).

5 Space filling model for menthol was obtained from Wikipedia Commons Public Domain at http://commons.wikimedia.org/wiki/Menthol (accessed Sept. 16, 2009).

In order to predict the three-dimensional molecular shape of a molecule or ion, you must first draw a *Lewis structure*. The Lewis structure gives information on skeletal structure (arrangement of atoms and what is bonded to what), and the location of valence electron pairs.

Method for Drawing Lewis Structures

1. Count the total number of valence electrons in the molecule or ion. If drawing the Lewis structure for an anion, add one electron for every negative charge. If drawing the Lewis structure for a cation, subtract one electron for every positive charge.

    Remember: The number of valence electrons for an A-Group element is numerically equal to the group number.

2. Draw a skeletal structure (what's bonded to what).

    *   The central atom is generally written first in the chemical formula.
    *   Hydrogen is never the central atom but is usually written first in acids.

3. Place one bond (one pair of electrons) between the central atom and each non-central atom to which it is to be bonded.

4. Surround each of the non-central atoms with an octet of electrons.

    Remember: a) a bond contributes two electrons when counting an octet and b) hydrogen is an exception to the octet rule and is surrounded by a maximum of two electrons.

5. Subtract the number of electrons in the drawing from the total. Place any remaining electrons on the central atom as a non-bonding pair(s) or lone pairs.

6. If the central atom does not have an octet of electrons, convert electron pairs on the non-central atoms to double or triple bonds until the central atom does have an octet.

    *   Hydrogen (H), boron (B), beryllium (Be), fluorine (F), and metals do not generally form multiple bonds. Hydrogen (H) is generally surrounded by 2 electrons, beryllium (Be) by 4 electrons, and boron (B) by 6 electrons (H, Be, and B are exceptions to the octet rule).

7. If the central atom in the previous step does not form multiple bonds (B, Be, or metals), then leave it short of an octet of electrons.

Method for Predicting Molecular Shapes

VSEPR Theory: *The Lewis structure* of a molecule or ion shows the placement of valence electron pairs on atoms. However, the Lewis structure alone does not give information on the 3D shape of a molecule or ion. **Valence Shell Electron Pair Repulsion (VSEPR) Theory** must be used to predict the 3D shape of a molecule or ion.

To use VSEPR theory, follow the steps outlined below:

1. Draw a correct Lewis structure for the molecule or ion.
2. Count up the total number of regions of electron density (E) surrounding the central atom.

    *   Each pair of non-bonding electrons (lone pair or U) counts as a region of electron density.
    *   Each bond counts as a region of electron density.

- However, double and triple bonds count as a single region of electron density.

3. Arrange the regions of electron density (E) in one of the five arrangements shown in Table 10-1. Since the regions of electron density are negatively charged and repel one another, they will adopt a three-dimensional arrangement so as to reside as far apart as possible.

4. The ***molecular shape*** is the resulting 3-D arrangement of atoms about the central atom in the molecule or ion. Molecular shapes for each of the five arrangements of electron density are given in Table 10-1.

   - The areas occupied by non-bonding electrons are not included in the molecular shape, but they do affect the overall shape.

   - You do not need to memorize the molecular shapes; they are easily reasoned from the arrangements of electron density.

Table 10.1: Summary of Arrangements of Regions of Electron Density and Molecular Shape.

Regions of Electron Density	Arrangement of Regions Electron Density and Bond Angles	Pairs of Nonbonding Electrons	Molecular Shape
2	linear (AE_2) 180°	0	linear
3	trigonal planar (AE_3) 120°	0 1	trigonal planar bent
4	tetrahedral (AE_4) 109.5°	0 1 2	tetrahedral trigonal pyramidal bent
5	trigonal bipyramidal (AE_5) Axial position / Equatorial positions / 90° / 120°	0 1 2 3	trigonal bipyramidal see-saw T-shaped linear
6	octahedral (AE_6) 90°	0 1 2	octahedral square pyramidal square planar

Method for Predicting Molecular Polarity

Generally speaking, a molecule is non-polar if:

- Its molecular shape is highly symmetric.
- The bond dipoles sum to zero.
- Its center of positive and negative charge coincide.

Example: BCl$_3$

- en=|2.0 – 3.0|=1.0 for B-Cl bonds
- B-Cl bonds are polar covalent
- Bond dipoles point from B to Cl
- All bond dipoles have the same strength
- Cl has partial negative charge
- B has partial positive charge

Bond dipoles are:

- Equal in magnitude and point in *symmetrically* opposed directions
- *Vector sum of bond dipoles is zero*
- Molecule is **NON-POLAR!**

A molecule is *polar* if:

- Its molecular shape is unsymmetric.
- Its bond dipoles do not sum to zero.
- Its centers of positive and negative charge do not coincide.

Example: BFCl$_2$

- en=|2.0 – 3.0|=1.0 for B-Cl bonds BUT en=|2.0 – 4.0|=2.0 for B-F bond
- B-Cl and B-F bonds are polar covalent
- Bond dipoles point from B to Cl and F
- Bond dipoles not of equal strength: B-F bond dipole is stronger than B-Cl
- Cl and F have partial negative charges, but flourine's is more negative
- B has partial positive charge

Bond dipoles are:

- *Unequal* in magnitude but still point in *symmetrically* opposed directions
- *Vector sum of bond dipoles is NOT zero*
- Molecule is **POLAR!**

To determine whether a molecule is polar or non-polar:

1. Draw a correct Lewis structure for the molecule or ion.

2. Use VSEPR theory to predict the molecular shape.

3. Predict polarity by looking at the molecular symmetry or vector sum of bond dipoles.

   • **Non-polar:** highly symmetric molecular shape and vector sum of bond dipoles = 0.

   • **Polar:** unsymmetric molecular shape and vector sum of bond dipoles ≠ 0.

You may work in pairs on this experiment but each student is to hand in his/her own copy of the entire experimental procedure and Data Report Sheets with all sections filled out. Be sure to:

• Completely answer all questions and fill in all blanks.

• Draw all Lewis structures.

• Show non-bonding electron pairs (or lone pairs) on both central and non-central atoms in Lewis structures, if present.

• Draw all three-dimensional molecular shapes.

• Show correct bond angles and three dimensions in molecular shapes.

   • Bonds represented by lengthened triangles indicate bonds/positions coming toward you and pointing out the front of the two-dimensional paper.

   • Bonds represented by lengthened dashed triangles or dashed lines indicate bonds/positions going away from you and pointing out the back of the two-dimensional paper.

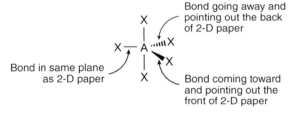

The Reason for Biodiesel: Intermolecular Forces

- Chemical splash goggles, gloves, and apron must be worn at all times.

- Sodium hydroxide is corrosive. Immediately wash all spills with excess water and inform the Teaching Assistant.

- Dispose of all liquid chemical waste in the designated liquid waste container under the hood. Do not dispose of organic waste down the drains.

- Do not use the Bunsen burner during any part of this experiment. Most organic compounds are highly flammable.

- Be careful of hot objects. Immediately place any burns under cold water and inform the Teaching Assistant.

- Tie back long hair and loose sleeves.

Materials

- sodium hydroxide, NaOH
- methanol, CH_3OH
- ethanol, C_2H_5OH
- propanol, C_3H_7OH
- butanol, C_4H_9OH
- octanol, $C_8H_{17}OH$

- pentane, C_5H_{12}
- octane, C_8H_{18}
- dodecane, $C_{12}H_{26}$
- vegetable oil
- biodiesel

Objectives

After completing this project, you will be able to:
- Evaluate the intermolecular forces acting within and between substances and identify the physical properties resulting from these forces.

- Predict trends in boiling points and vapor pressures of homologous compounds using differences in intermolecular forces.

- Explain how intermolecular forces affect vapor pressure, viscosity, and boiling point.

Experiment 11 | The Reason for Biodiesel: Intermolecular Forces   113

Introduction

Petroleum has fueled nearly a century of automobiles. Unfortunately, petroleum is also a toxic, nonrenewable resource that is extracted from limited numbers of geographic regions. The search for alternative liquid fuels in recent years has led to a great interest in *biodiesel*, a renewable, relatively nontoxic, compound that can be made from vegetable oils.

Vegetable oils themselves can be used directly as liquid fuels but suffer from several disadvantages. Primarily, oils tend to have high *viscosities* (i.e., high resistance to flow), and must be heated before they will flow quickly enough for common uses. Also, oils have very low *vapor pressures*[1] and high *boiling points*[2], so they must be heated to high temperatures before they can burn effectively. As a result of these physical properties, energy must be consumed to heat oils to a temperature where they can be used to produce energy, reducing the overall efficiency.

Through a simple chemical reaction, oils can be converted to fatty-acid methyl esters, also known as biodiesel. The reaction, shown below, breaks oil molecules into three smaller biodiesel molecules that are less viscous and easier to vaporize.

$$H_2C-O-\overset{\overset{O}{\|}}{C}-C_{15}H_{31}$$
$$CH-O-\overset{\overset{O}{\|}}{C}-C_{15}H_{31} \quad + \quad 3\ CH_3OH \quad \longrightarrow$$
$$H_2C-O-\overset{\overset{O}{\|}}{C}-C_{15}H_{31}$$

$$H_3C-O-\overset{\overset{O}{\|}}{C}-C_{15}H_{31} \qquad H_2C-OH$$
$$H_3C-O-\overset{\overset{O}{\|}}{C}-C_{15}H_{31} \quad + \quad HC-OH$$
$$H_3C-O-\overset{\overset{O}{\|}}{C}-C_{15}H_{31} \qquad H_2C-OH$$

oil   **methanol**
- high viscosity
- low vapor pressure
- high boiling point

fatty acid methyl esters (biodiesel)
- lower viscosity
- higher vapor pressure
- lower boiling point

glycerol

Scientific Background

Intermolecular Forces

Atoms or ions within a molecule or formula unit are held together by **intramolecular forces**, such as *covalent bonding* (attractions due to two atoms sharing a pair of electrons) or *ionic bonding* (attraction between ions of opposite charge). There are also forces that occur between molecules and ions that are not chemically bonded to each other. These are **intermolecular forces**. Without intermolecular forces, molecules would have no tendency to stay together; all compounds would be gases! Because of the close proximity of atoms and molecules in the condensed phases (solid and liquid phases), intermolecular forces are especially important in the condensed phases and influence condensed phase physical properties such as vapor pressure, boiling point, viscosity, and surface tension. Intermolecular forces have many other practical effects: they are responsible for friction and the structures of living cells.

---

1 Vapor pressure is the pressure exerted by the vapor in equilibrium with the liquid. The vapor pressure of a substance depends on temperature; as temperature increases, vapor pressure increases.

2 Boiling point is the temperature at which the vapor pressure of the liquid is equal to the atmospheric pressure. The boiling point of a sub-stance depends on atmospheric pressure; as atmospheric pressure increases, the boiling point increases.

The diagram below illustrates the difference between intramolecular and intermolecular forces.

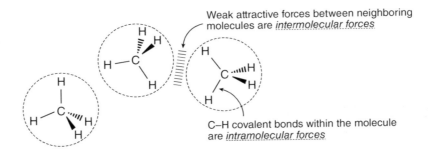

Weak attractive forces between neighboring molecules are *intermolecular forces*

C–H covalent bonds within the molecule are *intramolecular forces*

There are four major types of *intermolecular forces:*

1. ***Ion-Dipole Forces***—Exist between ions and polar molecules. For example, NaCl dissolved in polar water exhibits ion-dipole forces when one end of the polar water molecule is attracted to the oppositely charged ion from the salt.

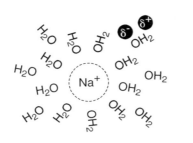

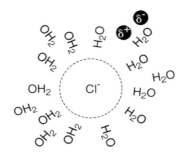

Polar water molecules surround the Na^+ cation and keep it dissolved. The water orients so negative end of polar molecule (oxygen end) is closer to positive charge of Na^+.

Polar water molecules surround the Cl^- anion and keep it dissolved. The water orients so positive end of polar molecule (hydrogen end) is closer to negative charge of Cl^-.

2. ***Dipole-Dipole forces***—Exist between molecules that have molecular dipoles (i.e., that are polar). All polar molecules exhibit dipole-dipole intermolecular forces.

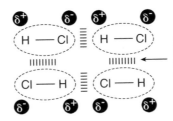

Dipole-dipole forces occur between neighboring molecules when polar molecules orient with unlike charges close.

3. **Hydrogen Bonding**—Is an extra-strong type of dipole-dipole intermolecular force that only occurs between molecules that contain a H atom directly bound to a N, O, or F atom.

3. Attraction between H atoms on one molecule and lone pair of electrons on atom (must be N, F, or O) in neighboring molecule constitutes **hydrogen bonding**.

1. N has en=3.0, one of the highest electronegativities. N pulls electrons from N–H bonds toward itself leaving H (en=2.1) nuclei as essentially bare protons unprotected by electrons.

2. H atoms with large partial positive charge are strongly attracted to lone pair of electrons on neighboring NH_3 molecule.

5. However, H_2S is polar so molecules of H_2S are held together by dipole-dipole forces in condensed phases.

4. Hydrogen bonding does NOT occur in H_2S because S (en=2.5) is not electronegative enough and does not as effectively pull electrons from S–H bonds toward itself. H (en=2.1) nuclei are partially protected by electrons in bond.

4. **London Dispersion Forces (LDFs)**—Are present in all substances. They are due to *instantaneous dipole-induced dipole forces.* An *instantaneous dipole* is a temporary dipole due to unsymmetric distribution of electrons about the nucleus. This *induces a momentary attractive dipole (induced dipole)* in a neighboring molecule or atom. In general, the strength of London dispersion forces within a chemical series depends on a) the sizes of the atoms (e.g., CF_4 vs. CBr_4); and b) the number of atoms in a molecule (within a homologous series) (e.g., C_2H_6 vs. C_3H_8).

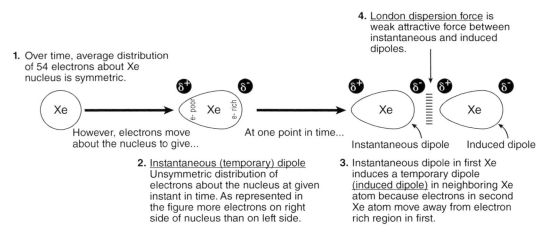

4. London dispersion force is weak attractive force between instantaneous and induced dipoles.

1. Over time, average distribution of 54 electrons about Xe nucleus is symmetric.

However, electrons move about the nucleus to give...

At one point in time...

Instantaneous dipole   Induced dipole

2. Instantaneous (temporary) dipole Unsymmetric distribution of electrons about the nucleus at given instant in time. As represented in the figure more electrons on right side of nucleus than on left side.

3. Instantaneous dipole in first Xe induces a temporary dipole (induced dipole) in neighboring Xe atom because electrons in second Xe atom move away from electron rich region in first.

Within a given compound, the relative strengths (strongest to weakest) of the more common types of intermolecular forces are:

Ion-Dipole > Hydrogen Bonding > Dipole-Dipole > London Dispersion

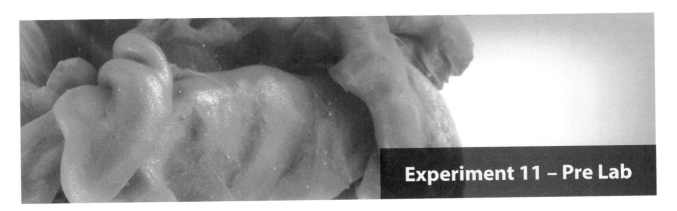

Examine the substances below. For each one, circle all type(s) of intermolecular forces that exist in its condensed phases (solid and liquid phases). Place an asterisk (*) next to the strongest. For compounds, you should draw Lewis structures and predict molecular shapes and molecular polarity.

He		KCl in water solution	
ion-dipole hydrogen bonding	dipole-dipole London dispersion	ion-dipole hydrogen bonding	dipole-dipole London dispersion
$N \equiv N$		SO_2	
ion-dipole hydrogen bonding	dipole-dipole London dispersion	ion-dipole hydrogen bonding	dipole-dipole London dispersion
NH_2OH		C_2H_6	
ion-dipole hydrogen bonding	dipole-dipole London dispersion	ion-dipole hydrogen bonding	dipole-dipole London dispersion
HBr		HF	
ion-dipole hydrogen bonding	dipole-dipole London dispersion	ion-dipole hydrogen bonding	dipole-dipole London dispersion
H - H		C_2H_2	
ion-dipole hydrogen bonding	dipole-dipole London dispersion	ion-dipole hydrogen bonding	dipole-dipole London dispersion
CH_3OH		$\overset{O}{\underset{}{\parallel}}\,\overset{O}{\underset{}{\parallel}}$ H – C – C – H	
ion-dipole hydrogen bonding	dipole-dipole London dispersion	ion-dipole hydrogen bonding	dipole-dipole London dispersion
IBr		CO_2	
ion-dipole hydrogen bonding	dipole-dipole London dispersion	ion-dipole hydrogen bonding	dipole-dipole London dispersion
CH_2F_2		$SeCl_4$	
ion-dipole hydrogen bonding	dipole-dipole London dispersion	ion-dipole hydrogen bonding	dipole-dipole London dispersion

Procedure

Part I: Biodiesel Synthesis

1. You will be working in pairs for this experiment. However, each student will turn in his/her own Data Report Sheet.

2. Into a 125-mL Erlenmeyer flask, place a stir bar, 2 pellets of NaOH, 20 mL of methanol, and 40 mL of vegetable, canola, or olive oil (as assigned by your Teaching Assistant). You will be making biodiesel from this oil!

   Type of oil sample used: _____

3. Place the flask on a stir plate and stir briskly (without splashing), so that the oil and methanol layers are efficiently blended.

4. Place a small watch glass, convex down or U, over the mouth of the flask.

5. Use a medium setting to heat the mixture. Do not go above 200 °C. Your goal is to dissolve the NaOH and heat the mixture to a gentle boil. At the proper heat setting, you should see methanol condensing on the neck of the flask. If the watch glass is "bumping," then the methanol is boiling too fast and methanol vapor is pushing up the watch glass; in this case the heat should be turned down. Once you observe the methanol condensing on the neck of the flask, heat the mixture for 30 minutes more. **At this point, proceed to the Procedure, Parts II and III and return periodically to check on the progress of the biodiesel synthesis!**

   Start time: _____   Stop time: _____

6. After the 30 minutes of heating is completed, take off the watch glass and carefully remove the flask from the hot plate. To avoid burning your hand, use your blue towel as hand protection or use tongs (if available). Place the flask on the lab bench until it has cooled to near room temperature.

7. There should be two layers of liquid in the flask. The top layer is the less-dense biodiesel. The denser bottom layer contains NaOH, glycerol, and unreacted methanol. Pipet the biodiesel layer from the flask into a small beaker. Save the biodiesel for the viscosity measurement detailed later in Procedure, Part III.

Part II: Relative Rates of Evaporation

Why is evaporation a cooling process?

Molecules in the liquid phase are held together by intermolecular forces of attraction. If enough energy is present to overcome these intermolecular forces of attraction, then molecules will escape from the liquid to the gas phase and evaporation occurs. Only molecules with the highest energy will have enough energy to escape into the gas phase. When a liquid evaporates, it therefore loses molecules with higher energy. Due to the conservation of energy, the liquid molecules left behind must have lower energy, which means that it has a lower temperature.

Think About It: Two similar pieces of cloth are saturated with two different liquids (A and B) at the same temperature of 25 °C. After 10 minutes, the temperature of the cloth saturated with liquid A is 22 °C, while that saturated with liquid B is 24 °C.

Which liquid evaporated at a faster rate?   A   B   (circle one)

Which liquid had the stronger intermolecular forces of attraction?   A   B   (circle one)

Why? _____

1. Plug in and turn on the SPARK unit.

2. Once the SPARK software initializes, the screen will ask you to plug in a sensor. Plug the temperature sensor into the top of the unit.

3. From the options that appear on the screen, choose "Temperature" and press "Show."

4. A graph will appear. The SPARK is now ready to collect data.

5. Obtain a precut rectangle of filter paper, a piece of wire, and in a test tube no more than 10 drops of one the liquids listed in Table 11-1. You just need enough liquid to saturate the filter paper.

6. Wrap the filter paper around the end of the temperature probe, being sure to cover the very end of the probe. Use the wire to secure the filter paper to the probe. Temperature is only measured at the tip of the probe. Because your body heat may heat up the temperature probe, wait for a short time before proceeding. Be careful: Temperature probes are delicate and easily damaged.

7. Place the covered tip of the temperature probe into the liquid in the test tube to just saturate the filter paper with the liquid.

8. Press the green ▶ button on the SPARK to begin data collection.

9. After one minute, lift the probe out of the liquid and lay it horizontally on the lab bench, with at least the last three inches of the probe extending over the edge of the bench. Monitor the temperature. Autoscale as needed.

What process is happening to the liquid on the filter paper? _____

_____

How does this process affect the temperature of the liquid left on the filter paper? Why?

_____

_____

_____

10. The temperature should drop and reach a plateau. After the plateau, the temperature will rise slowly as heat leaks in from the surroundings.

11. Once the temperature has started to rise, press the red ▶ button on the unit to stop data collection.

12. Record the initial temperature, T_i, as the temperature of the probe immediately before you removed it from the test tube. Record the final temperature, T_f, as the lowest temperature reached by the probe as the liquid evaporated from the filter paper. Calculate the change in temperature caused by evaporation of the liquid, T_i-T_f.

   • This temperature change is a measure of the strength of the intermolecular forces. Is it a direct or inverse relationship? _____

13. Dispose of the filter paper in the labeled container under the hood and the liquid in the liquid waste container.

14. Obtain a new liquid sample of those remaining in Table 11-1 and a new piece of filter paper. Either use a clean test tube or rinse the previously used test tube with a small amount of the liquid itself before obtaining your 10 drops. Repeat the procedure for each compound in Table 11-1.

Part III: Measurement of Relative Viscosity

Why is viscosity a physical property?

If there are strong intermolecular forces of attraction between molecules, then it will be very hard for one molecule to slide past another. This attraction between molecules sliding past one another is the physical origin of viscosity, or resistance of a liquid to flow.

1. Clamp a buret to a ring stand; place a beaker under the buret tip to collect waste.

2. Use your graduated cylinder to obtain about 18–20 mL of one of the liquid compounds given in Table 11-2.

3. Fill your buret to the 10-mL mark with the liquid compound. Be sure the buret tip is completely filled with liquid and that air bubbles have been removed from inside the buret tip.

4. Open the stopcock completely to allow the liquid to drain from the buret into a waste beaker. Record the time (use a stopwatch) it takes for the meniscus to pass between the 15-mL mark and the 25-mL mark.

    *   This time is related to the viscosity of the liquid, which in turn is related to the strength of intermolecular forces.

    *   If the liquid takes an exceedingly long time (> 8 minutes) to drain through the buret, your buret tip may be clogged. Ask your Teaching Assistant for assistance.

5. Repeat for each liquid in Table 11-2. Use the same buret for all measurements!

    *   Be sure to rinse the buret and stopcock tip with 1–2 mL of the new liquid to be tested prior to filling the buret to the 10-mL mark with the next liquid. Dispose of this rinse solution in the proper container.

6. In addition, measure the viscosity of the oil (vegetable, canola, olive) that you used for your biodiesel synthesis in Procedure, Part I. Put your results in Table 11-3.

7. Measure the viscosity of the biodiesel that you synthesized in Procedure, Part I. Put your results in Table 11-3.

8. After completing the table, close the stopcock on the buret and fill the buret with acetone. Put a waste beaker under the buret and open the stopcock to drain the acetone. This step removes organic compounds from the barrel of the buret.

9. **Double-check any calculations and be sure you have expressed all experimental measurements with the proper number of significant figures and units.** Based on what you know about intermolecular forces, do you have the correct trends? If not, you may need to repeat that part of the experiment. Use your knowledge of intermolecular forces and strengths of intermolecular forces to give complete answers (use complete sentences for explanations) for the questions in the Data Report Sheet, Part II. Have your Teaching Assistant verify your completion of this experiment by signing. Rip off and hand in the Data Report Sheets, Parts I and II for grading. Each student is to hand in his/her own Data Report Sheet. However, students working in pairs should include their partner's name on the Data Report Sheet. Dispose of all chemical wastes as indicated by your Teaching Assistant.

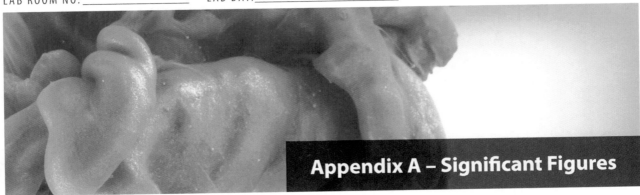

Appendix A – Significant Figures

1. Determine the number of significant figures in each of the following measured numbers.

    a. 6.751 in

    b. 30.07 L

    c. 54.52 s

    d. 0.157 g

    e. 0.106 kg

    f. 0.1209 ng

    g. 28.0 J

    h. 0.0067 cal

    i. 2.690 M

    j. 20.00 mL

    k. 0.0230 mol

    l. 43.07%

    m. 0.070 N

    n. 4000.0 ppt

    o. 0.09050 m

2. Carry out the following mathematical operations of measured numbers. Express your answers with the correct number of significant figures.

I. Addition

a. 675.1 + 4.458 =

b. 5 + 0.03 + 2.0 =

c. 16.5 + 8 + 4.37 =

d. 27.54 + 3.2 + 2.6 =

e. 13.22 + 10.00 + 9.6 =

f. 2.36 + 3.38 + 0.355 + 1.06 =

g. 0.0853 + 0.0547 + 2.446 + 0.009 =

h. 25.37 + 6.850 + 15.07 + 8.056 =

i. 24.43 + 4.207 + 0.0736 + 0.0041 =

j. 205 + 43 + 6.2 + 7.34 =

II. Subtraction

    a.   23.27 - 12.058 =

    b.   13.57 - 6.3 =

    c.   350.0 - 200. =

    d.   27.68 - 14.369 =

    e.   42.38 - 29.6 =

    f.   0.047 - 0.0345 =

    g.   1.255 - 0.040 =

    h.   27.5 - 7.25 =

    i.   2500.0 - 0.078 =

    j.   4.785 - 2.1 =

III. Multiplication

    a. $2.6 \times 3.78 =$

    b. $0.036 \times 0.02 =$

    c.   (1.35)(0.04) =

    d.   (3.15)(2.5)(4.00) =

    e.   (6.43)(5.32)(4.2) =

    f. $35.7 \times 0.78 \times 2.3 =$

    g. $0.050 \times 0.027 \times 0.8222 =$

    h. $0.006 \times 8888 \times 25 =$

    i. $25.00 \times 10.00 \times 2.00 =$

    j. $3.54 \times 4.8 \times 0.5421 =$

IV. Division

    a. $35 \div 0.62 =$

    b. $0.58 \div 6.1 =$

    c. $3.76 \div 39.02 =$

    d. $0.075 \div 0.030 =$

    e. $0.25 \div 21 =$

    f.   30.98/13.6 =

    g.   0.099/0.11 =

    h.   3.1416/12.4 =

    i.   64.36/13.6 =

    j.   4569/13 =

V. Mixed Operations

a. $(4.52 + 6.278) - 1.41 =$

b. $(55.057 + 2.12) - 40.3 =$

c. $3.7 + 4.75 + 10.555 - 7.9 =$

d. $(4.44 \div 1.11) \times (6.02 \div 1.2) =$

e. $1.238 \div (1.85 \times 1.245) =$

f. $\dfrac{2.5 \times 1.52}{2.17 \times 5.018} =$

g. $32 \times \dfrac{732}{760.} \times \dfrac{273}{292} =$

h. $\dfrac{7.5 \times 0.012}{5.5} =$

i. $\dfrac{2.78 + 2.695 + 2.72 + 2.75}{4.00} =$

j. $\dfrac{(14.85 - 12.57) - 0.92}{12.6} =$

Appendix B – Exponential Numbers

Exponential numbers are convenient for expressing very large and very small numbers. They are especially convenient when performing multiplication and division. Exponential numbers are frequently used to describe quantities; for example, there are 6.02×10^{23} oxygen molecules per mole (32 g) of oxygen; the Van der Waals radius of hydrogen is 1.2×10^{-8} cm; the velocity of light in a vacuum is 2.9979×10^{10} cm/s, etc.

Standard Exponential Form (Scientific Notation)

Numbers may be written by showing the number of tens that may be factored and writing this as an exponent of 10, for example, $4681 = 4.681 \times 10 \times 10 \times 10 = 4.681 \times 10^3$. When written in the form 4.681×10^3, this number is expressed in *standard exponential form*, also called *scientific notation*. In standard exponential form, there is one digit to the left of the decimal point; the number of digits to the right of the decimal place is determined by the number of significant figures. Furthermore, the digit term (the term to the left of 10 and its exponent) is always a number between one and ten. The following examples will give you some idea as to the use of exponents. The first example is used to illustrate the difference between standard exponential form and exponential form; all other examples show conversion to standard exponential form.

EXAMPLE 1

$2{,}980{,}000{,}000 \quad = 2.98 \times 10^9 \qquad$ (standard exponential form; digit term between 1–10)

$(3\ \text{sig. figs.}) \qquad = 29.8 \times 10^8 \qquad$ (exponential form; digit term greater than 10)

$\qquad\qquad\qquad = 0.298 \times 10^{10} \quad$ (exponential form; digit term less than 1)

OTHER EXAMPLES

298	$= 2.98 \times 10^2$	0.298	$= 2.98 \times 10^{-1}$
29.8×10^{-2}	$= 2.98 \times 10^{-1}$	0.0000298	$= 2.98 \times 10^{-5}$
298×10^2	$= 2.98 \times 10^4$	0.00298×10^{-3}	$= 2.98 \times 10^{-6}$

In the examples shown above, you will notice that each time the decimal is moved one place to the left, the exponent of 10 is increased by one. Conversely, each time the decimal is moved one place to the right, the exponent of 10 is decreased by one. You can use this shorthand method to quickly convert any number to standard exponential form.

1. Without using your calculator, express the following numbers in standard exponential form:

1,000 (1 sf) = _____   0.0072 = _____

0.001 = _____   320.0 = _____

4,728 = _____   0.105 = _____

6,000,000 (4 sf) = _____   93,000,000 (2 sf) = _____

$3,567.0 \times 10^2$ = _____ 0.00030×10^{-4} = _____

Multiplication of Exponential Numbers

To multiply numbers expressed as powers of 10, the digit terms are multiplied and the exponents of 10 are added algebraically, as shown below.

$(1.0 \times 10^a)(1.0 \times 10^b)$ $= 1.0 \times 10^{(a+b)}$

$(1.0 \times 10^5)(2.0 \times 10^9)$ $= 2.0 \times 10^{(5+9)}$ $= 2.0 \times 10^{14}$

$(2.0 \times 10^5)(3.0 \times 10^{-4})$ $= 6.0 \times 10^{(5+(-4))}$ $= 6.0 \times 10^1$

2. Without using your calculator, evaluate the following multiplications and express the final answer in standard exponential form. To simplify your calculation, convert all numbers to standard exponential form before performing the multiplication.

$(0.003)(4.0 \times 10^5)$ = _____

$(0.008)(0.002)$ = _____

$(1.50 \times 10^{-5})(2.0 \times 10^{-4})$ = _____

Division of Exponential Numbers

To divide numbers expressed as powers of 10, the digit terms are divided and the exponents of 10 are subtracted algebraically, as shown below.

$(1.0 \times 10^a) \div (1.0 \times 10^b)$ $= 1.0 \times 10^{(a-b)}$

$(3.0 \times 10^4) \div (1.5 \times 10^2)$ $= 2.0 \times 10^{(4-2)}$ $= 2.0 \times 10^2$

$(6.0 \times 10^{-8}) \div (2.0 \times 10^2)$ $= 3.0 \times 10^{(-8-2)}$ $= 3.0 \times 10^{-10}$

$(8.6 \times 10^{-8}) \div (2.0 \times 10^{-2})$ $= 4.3 \times 10^{(-8-(-2))}$ $= 4.3 \times 10^{-6}$

3. Without using your calculator, evaluate the following divisions and express the final answer in standard exponential form.

$(6.0 \times 10^6) \div (3.0 \times 10^4)$ = _____

$(7.5 \times 10^9) \div (2.5 \times 10^3)$ = _____

$(7.5 \times 10^{-9}) \div (2.5 \times 10^{-3})$ = _____

$(7.5 \times 10^9) \div (2.5 \times 10^{-3})$ = _____

$(7.5 \times 10^{-9}) \div (2.5 \times 10^3)$ = _____

4. Without using your calculator, perform the following operations and express the final answer in standard exponential form.

$$\frac{(1.0 \times 10^4)(1.0 \times 10^5)}{(1.0 \times 10^2)} = \underline{\hspace{9cm}}$$

$$\frac{(6.0 \times 10^{-4})(6.0 \times 10^3)}{(3.6 \times 10^2)} = \underline{\hspace{9cm}}$$

$$\frac{(8.2 \times 10^9)(6.0 \times 10^6)}{(4.1 \times 10^5)} = \underline{\hspace{9cm}}$$

$$\frac{(8.2 \times 10^{-4})(6.0 \times 10^{-4})}{(4.92 \times 10^1)} = \underline{\hspace{9cm}}$$

$$\frac{(6 \times 10^5)(4 \times 10^3)(2 \times 10^2)}{(3 \times 10^3)(2 \times 10^6)} = \underline{\hspace{9cm}}$$

Addition and Subtraction

To add or subtract exponential numbers, the exponents of 10 must be the same. If different, the exponents must be made the same. Once the exponents are made the same, the digits are added or subtracted as re-quired. The example given below shows the steps involved in adding or subtracting numbers in exponential form.

Add: 4.15×10^{-2} and 3.67×10^{-1}

Step 1: Convert to the same exponent of 10. As a general rule, convert the smaller exponent to the larger. Converting the larger exponent to the smaller works as well, but in many cases gives an answer that as a final step must be converted to standard exponential form.

$$\begin{aligned} 4.14 \times 10^{-2} \\ + 3.67 \times 10^{-1} \end{aligned} \quad \text{becomes} \quad \begin{aligned} 0.414 \times 10^{-1} \\ + 3.67 \times 10^{-1} \end{aligned}$$

Step 2: Next add the numbers and round to the correct number of decimal places. Remember, in addition and subtraction, the number of decimal places on the answer is limited by the original number with the least number of decimal places.

$$\begin{array}{ll} 4.14 \times 10^{-1} & \text{(3 decimals)} \\ + 3.67 \times 10^{-1} & \text{(2 decimals)} \\ \hline 4.084 \times 10^{-1} & \text{becomes } 4.08 \times 10^{-1} \text{ when correctly rounded to 2 decimal places} \end{array}$$

5. Without using your calculator, evaluate the following additions and subtractions and express the final answers in standard exponential form. Remember to convert the numbers to the same exponent before performing the addition or subtraction.

$(6.0 \times 10^5) + (6.0 \times 10^4)$ = _____

$(5.0 \times 10^{-3}) + (6.0 \times 10^{-5})$ = _____

$(7.02 \times 10^5) + (5 \times 10^3)$ = _____

$(6.02 \times 10^{23}) + (6.02 \times 10^{24}) + (6.02 \times 10^{22})$ = _____

$(6.02 \times 10^{24}) - (6.02 \times 10^{23})$ = _____

$(1.5 \times 10^{-5}) - (2.5 \times 10^{-6})$ = _____

$(6.02 \times 10^{-2}) - (6.00 \times 10^{-2})$ = _____

Calculators and Exponential Numbers

When using a calculator, one source of error is incorrect entry of exponential numbers. For example, the speed of light (2.9979×10^8 m/s) is a typical exponential number used in numerous calculations in chemistry and physics. When entering this number into your calculator, use the following series of keystrokes: 1) input the digit term: 2.9979; 2) press the EE or EXP button (this informs your calculator that an exponential number is being entered); and 3) input the exponent: 8. This general procedure applies for most brands of calculators. However, you may need to consult your calculator manual on the correct procedure for inputting exponential numbers into your calculator.

Appendix C – Chemical Nomenclature

Introduction

The vocabulary of chemistry is necessary for communication within the field of chemistry. Ideas can be communicated only when all parties are familiar with the vocabulary. Thus a study of the naming or *nomenclature* of chemical compounds is essential for all students undertaking the study of chemistry.

Chemical symbols are used to represent names of elements, e.g., He is used to represent the element helium. *Chemical formulas* are used to represent the composition of chemical compounds, polyatomic ions, elements, and other pure substances, e.g., the chemical formula Cl_2 is used to represent the polyatomic element chlorine, while the chemical formula K_3N is used to represent the chemical compound potassium nitride. Chemistry students should become familiar with writing names from chemical formulas and chemical formulas from names.

In this section you will learn to name binary and ternary inorganic compounds. *Binary compounds* are those that are composed of two different elements. *Ternary compounds* are those composed of three different elements. The following list: HBr, H_2SO_4, $Al_2(SO_4)_3$, NH_3, Mg_2Si, and F_2 contains __1__ binary compound and __2__ ternary compounds. The substance in the above list that is not a compound but with a composition expressed by a formula is __3__ .

Inorganic compounds are those compounds not classified as organic. Organic compounds are defined as hydro-carbons and their derivatives. As the name implies, hydrocarbons contain the elements carbon and hydrogen, e.g., the compounds C_8H_{18}, $C_{20}H_{40}$, and C_2H_2 are hydrocarbons and, hence, organic compounds. A *hydrocarbon derivative* contains carbon, hydrogen, and one or more other elements, e.g., the compounds C_2H_5OH, C_6H_5SH, and $C_5H_{11}NO$ are hydrocarbon derivatives and, hence, organic compounds. The nomenclature of organic com-pounds will be covered in a later course. The following list: CO_2, PBr_3, C_3H_8, $AlCl_3$, $C_5H_{10}O$, N_2H_4, and $C_6H_4Cl_2$ contains __4__ organic compounds and __5__ inorganic compounds.

Before naming an inorganic compound, the compound must first be classified as one of the following types: ionic compound, molecular (covalent) compound, binary acid, or oxyacid. The rules for naming an inorganic compound depend on the type of compound, i.e., ionic compounds have slightly different names than molecular compounds.

An *ionic compound* is composed of a metal and a non-metal, a metal and a polyatomic ion, a polyatomic ion and a non-metal, or two polyatomic ions, e.g., CaS, $Ba(NO_3)_2$, $(NH_4)_2S$, and NH_4NO_3 are ionic compounds. A *molecular (covalent) compound* is composed of two or more non-metals, e.g., P_2O_5, NH_3, and ClBr are molecular compounds. A *binary acid* is composed of hydrogen and one other non-metal element, e.g., HBr and H_2S, while an *oxyacid* is composed of hydrogen, oxygen, and one other element, e.g., $HBrO_2$ and H_3PO_4. To indicate the presence of either a binary acid or an oxyacid, hydrogen is written first in the chemical formula. Notice this practice in the preceding examples. In the following list: H_2SO_3, $ZnSO_4$, HCl, XeF_4, Na_2O, BCl_3, H_2Se, and HNO_2, __6__ are ionic compounds, __7__ are molecular compounds, __8__ are binary acids, and __9__ are oxyacids.

Nomenclature of Ionic Compounds: Metal Cation of Non-Variable Charge

If the ionic compound contains a metal cation with a non-variable charge (Group IA, IIA metals, and Al), the charge of the metal cation is not specified in the name. By convention the metal (or more electropositive species) is written first in the chemical formula, whereas the non-metal (or more electronegative species) is written second.

Nomenclature of Ionic Compounds: Metal Cation of Non-Variable Charge

a. Name the metal cation, i.e., the more electropositive species.

b. Name the non-metal anion or polyatomic ion, i.e., the more electronegative species.

c. Add "-ide" to the stem of the non-metal name. Note: Do not change the ending of a polyatomic ion.

Thus, to name KBr,... the metal, K, potassium, is named first followed by the non-metal, Br, bromine, which is named second. At this point, the unfinished name of the compound is potassium bromine. Third, and last, "-ide" is added to the stem of the non-metal name. The stem for bromine is brom-, and adding "-ide" converts it to bromide. As a result, the completed name for the compound KBr is potassium bromide. This process is represented below for KBr, CaC_2, and $NaNO_2$.

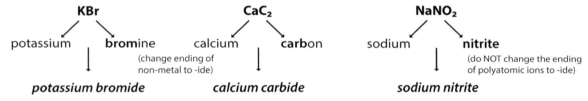

In forming a stem, the last syllable in the name of the element is dropped, i.e., "brom-" is the stem for bromine, whereas __10__ is the stem for carbon. The stem never ends in a vowel. Should the stem end in a vowel or a vowel sound, the vowel is also dropped to make the stem. In making a stem from nitrogen, dropping the last syllable gives "nitro." Since "o" is a vowel it is also dropped to give the stem "nitr-" and a binary compound in which nitrogen is the more electronegative element would be called nitride. The stem for oxygen would be __11__ since "oxy" ends in a vowel sound. The stem for chlorine is "chlor-"; whereas __12__ is the stem for iodine. The stems for arsenic and selenium would be __13__ and __14__, respectively. There are exceptions to the rule. Sulfur and phosphorus follow neither rule. The stem for sulfur is "sulf-", while the stem for phosphorus is __15__.

Using the above rules, name the following ionic compounds:

MgF_2	__16__	$Al_2(SO_4)_3$	__19__	CaO	__22__
KH	__17__	Sr_3P_2	__20__	$LiNO_3$	__23__
Ca_3N_2	__18__	AlF_3	__21__		

Nomenclature of Ionic Compounds: Metal Cation of Variable Charge

For some elements, two or more compounds may be formed depending on the charge of the metal. For example, copper can have a charge of 11 or 12 and can form the two chlorides CuCl and $CuCl_2$. The rules given above are insufficient to distinguish CuCl from CuC_{12} since with these rules both would be named copper chloride. Therefore, if the ionic compound contains a metal cation with a variable charge (transition or post-transition metal), then name the compound via the Stock or IUPAC (International Union of Pure and Applied Chemistry) System as outlined below.

Nomenclature of Ionic Compounds via IUPAC System: Metal Cation of Variable Charge

a. Name the metal cation, i.e., the more electropositive species.

b. Immediately after this name with no space, use a Roman numeral to specify the charge on the metal cation. Enclose the Roman numeral in parentheses.

c. Name the non-metal anion or polyatomic ion, i.e., the more electronegative species.

d. Add "-ide" to the stem of the non-metal name. Note: Do not change the ending of a polyatomic ion.

In this case, the charge on the metal cation is specified in the name. Thus, to name CrO, the metal, Cr, chromium, is named first followed by the chromium's charge of +2 specified with a Roman numeral resulting in chromium(II). The non-metal, O, oxygen, is named second. At this point, the unfinished name of the compound is chromium(II) oxygen. Last, "-ide" is added to the stem of the non-metal name. The stem for oxygen is ox-, and adding "-ide" converts it to oxide. As a result, the completed name for the compound CrO is chromium(II) oxide. The positive charge on the metal ion is determined by the total negative charge(s) of the anion(s). Group VIIA elements are assigned a –1 charge in binary ionic compounds; Group VIA, a –2 charge; and Group VA, a –3 charge. Using the above rules, name the following ionic compounds:

Cr_2O_3	__24__	$Ni(CN)_2$	__27__	SnF_4	__30__
CrO_3	__25__	$FeCl_3$	__28__	$Co(OH)_3$	__31__
$FeCl_2$	__26__	SnF_2	__29__		

An older system for naming ionic compounds when the metal has a variable charge adds the suffixes "-ous" and "-ic" to the stem of the Latin (or English) name for the metal. The "-ous" ending is used to signify the lower of two charges, while the "-ic" ending is used to signify the higher of two charges. In the old system, Latin names are used for the metals given below. The English name is used for all other metals.

Chemical Symbol	English Name	Latin Name
Fe	Iron	Ferrum
Sn	Tin	Stannum
Pb	Lead	Plumbum
Cu	Copper	Cuprum
Au	Gold	Aurum

The procedure for naming ionic compounds with a metal of variable charge via the old system is outlined below. Thus, to name $FeCl_2$ and $FeCl_3$, the Latin name for iron, ferrum, is used. The charge of iron in $FeCl_2$ and $FeCl_3$ is +2 and +3, respectively. Thus, in $FeCl_2$, the iron has the lower of two charges, "-ous" is added to the Latin name for iron and ferrum becomes ferrous. The complete name for $FeCl_2$ is ferrous chloride. In $FeCl_3$, the iron has the higher of two charges, "-ic" is added to the Latin name for iron and ferrum becomes ferric. The complete name for $FeCl_3$ is ferric chloride.

Nomenclature of Ionic Compounds via Old System: Metal Cation of Variable Charge

a. Name the metal cation using the Latin name, if available, otherwise use the English name.

b. Specify the charge on the metal by adding the following suffixes to the stem of the metal name:

   "-ous" metal with lower of two positive charges
   "-ic"   metal with higher of two positive charges

c. Name the non-metal anion or polyatomic ion, i.e., the more electronegative species.

d. Add "-ide" to the stem of the non-metal name. Note: Do not change the ending of a polyatomic ion.

Name the following pairs of ionic compounds using the older "-ous/-ic" system:

SnS_2	__32__	$CuSO_3$	__35__	$TiCl_4$	__38__
SnS	__33__	Sb_2O_3	__36__	$TiCl_3$	__39__
Cu_2SO_3	__34__	Sb_2O_5	__37__		

There are a few drawbacks to the old system that have resulted in its replacement by the IUPAC system. If the metal can exist in more than two charge states, the older system using "-ous" and "-ic" can only name two. For example, four oxides of manganese, MnO, MnO_2, MnO_3, and Mn_2O_7, with Mn charges of +2, +4, +6, and +7, respectively, can form. The older system can only name two of the four. In the Stock or IUPAC system all four ox-ides of manganese have a distinct name. The IUPAC system is especially useful in naming compounds in which two charge states appear in one species. For example, in Fe_3O_4, two of the irons have a charge of +3, while one has a charge of +2. As a result, the name for Fe_3O_4 in the IUPAC system would be iron(II, III) oxide. The old system has no rules for naming this compound. In Pb_3O_4, two of the leads have a charge of +2, while one has a charge of +4. As a result, the name of Pb_3O_4 in the IUPAC system would be __40__ .

Obtaining a Chemical Formula from a Chemical Name

To proceed from the chemical name of an ionic compound to the chemical formula, it must be remembered that the formula unit is neutral. For example, what chemical formula is specified by the chemical name barium iodide? First, write the chemical symbols for the two elements. Barium specifies Ba, and iodide specifies I. Next, assign charges to the ions. Since Ba is a metal in Group IIA, its charge is +2. Since I is a non-metal in Group VIIA, its charge is –1. Last, combine the ions to give a neutral formula unit using the smallest set of whole number subscripts. To give a neutral compound two I^{-1} are needed for every one Ba^{+2} and the neutral formula unit becomes Ba_2. This process is represented on the following page for barium iodide and copper(I) nitride. For compounds containing polyatomic ions, one must memorize the ions and their charges (NH_4^+, NO_3^-, SO_4^{-2}, PO_4^{-3}, ClO_3^-, CO_3^{-2}, etc.).

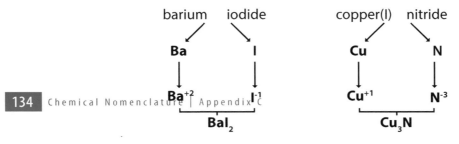

Using the preceding process, give neutral formula units for the following ionic compounds:

barium sulfide	__41__	sodium sulfide	__45__
aluminum bromide	__42__	cesium chloride	__46__
magnesium arsenide	__43__	aluminum phosphide	__47__
strontium perchlorate	__44__	rubidium phosphate	__48__

Nomenclature of Molecular Compounds

Molecular compounds are named as outlined below. In most compounds, the more electropositive element, i.e., the element that lies farthest to the left in the periodic table, is written first in the chemical formula; whereas, the more electronegative element, i.e., the element that lies farthest to the right in the periodic table, is written second. Greek prefixes (see the table below) are used to specify the number of each type of atom in molecular compound.

Nomenclature of Molecular Compounds

a. Name the more electropositive element, i.e., the element that lies farthest to the left in the periodic table.

b. Name the more electronegative element, i.e., the element that lies farthest to the right in the periodic table, and add an "-ide" ending.

c. Add Greek prefixes to both names to specify the number of each type of element present.

Number	Greek Prefix	Number	Greek Prefix	Number	Greek Prefix
1	mono-	5	penta-	9	nona-
2	di-	6	hexa-	10	deca-
3	tri-	7	hepta		
4	tetra-	8	octa		

Thus, N_2O_5 is dinitrogen pentoxide, while N_2O_4 is dinitrogen tetroxide. Notice that to avoid the placement of two vowels in adjacent positions, the "a" of the "penta-" and "tetra-" prefixes is dropped when forming pent-oxide and tetroxide. In general, when addition of a Greek prefix to the name of an element will result in two adjacent vowels, the vowel of the Greek prefix is dropped. For the first element named, the "mono-" Greek prefix is understood and not included; however, for the second element named, the "mono-" Greek prefix is included. Thus, NO_2 is nitrogen dioxide, while N_2O is dinitrogen monoxide.

Using the preceding rules, name the following molecular compounds:

P_4O_{10}	__49__	PBr_5	__52__	Cl_2O	__55__
C_3O_2	__50__	P_4S_3	__53__	CO	__56__
PCl_3	__51__	XeF_4	__54__		

To proceed from the chemical name of a molecular compound to the chemical formula is relatively simple. The name of a molecular compound gives the number and type of each element present. For example, what chemical formula is specified by the name dichlorine heptoxide? The name indicates that two atoms of chlorine and seven atoms of oxygen are combined in one molecule. Thus the chemical formula of dichlorine heptoxide is Cl_2O_7.

Give the correct chemical formula for the following molecular compounds:

carbon dioxide	__57__	dioxygen difluoride	__61__
sulfur hexafluoride	__58__	tetrasulfur tetranitride	__62__
iodine monochloride	__59__	chlorine trifluoride	63
sulfur trioxide	__60__	silicon tetrachloride	__64__

Nomenclature of Binary Acids and Binary Hydrides

Binary hydrides of the non-metals, e.g., HCl and H_2S, are named similar to ionic compounds. Hydrogen is named first followed by the non-metal with the "-ide" ending. Greek prefixes are not used and charges are not specified. Thus, gaseous HCl and H_2S are named hydrogen chloride and hydrogen sulfide, respectively. However, many of the binary hydrides of the non-metals, when dissolved in aqueous solution, yield acidic solutions. This is especially true of those non-metals in Groups VIA and VIIA. Aqueous solutions of these binary hydrogen compounds are named as binary acids as shown below.

Nomenclature of Binary Acids

a. The non-metal name is used to make a stem.

b. The prefix "hydro-" and suffix "-ic" are added to the stem.

c. The word "acid" is added.

Thus, to name an aqueous solution of HCl, denoted as HCl(aq), the non-metal stem "chlor" is used as the base of the name. The prefix "hydro-" and suffix "-ic" are added to this base to give hydrochloric. The word acid is appended resulting in hydrochloric acid as the name for HCl(aq). Likewise, an aqueous solution of H_2S, denoted as H_2S(aq), is named hydrosulfuric acid.

Using the above rules, name the following binary hydride and binary acids:

HBr(g) __65__   HBr(aq) __66__   H2Se(aq) __67__   HF(aq) __68__

Many students write the formula H_2SO_4 for hydrosulfuric acid. This is incorrect. Notice that the "hydro-" prefix is only used to designate binary acids, NOT oxyacids. Therefore, the "hydro-" prefix should not be used for the oxyacid H_2SO_4. The name hydrosulfuric acid designates a binary acid containing the elements hydrogen and sulfur. The correct chemical formula of hydrosulfuric acid is neutral. The hydrogen can be thought of as H^+, while the sulfur can be thought of as S^{-2}. In order for the binary acid to be neutral, two H^+ combine with one S^{-2} to give the neutral binary acid H_2S.

Nomenclature of Oxyacids

The difficulty in naming oxyacids is that many elements can form two or more different oxyacids. For example, four oxyacids of chlorine exist: $HClO$, $HClO_2$, $HClO_3$, and $HClO_4$. Each of these four oxyacids must be given a distinct name. Oxyacids are named as outlined below.

a. The non-metal name is used to make a stem.

b. If *two different oxyacids* are formed by the element, specify the oxyacid by adding the following suffixes to the stem:

"-ous"   oxyacid with least oxygen

"-ic"   oxyacid with most oxygen

If *four different oxyacids* are formed by the element, specify the oxyacid by adding the following prefixes and suffixes to the stem as the number of oxygen atoms steadily increases:

"hypo-""-ous" oxyacid with least oxygen

   "-ous"

   "-ic"

"per-" "-ic" oxyacid with most oxygen

c. The word "acid" is added.

For example, sulfur forms two oxyacids with chemical formulas H_2SO_3 and H_2SO_4. To name aqueous solutions of H_2SO_3 and H_2SO_4, the suffixes "-ous" and "-ic", respectively, are added to the "sulfur" stem followed by the word acid. As a result, H_2SO_3, with the least number of oxygen atoms, is named sulfurous acid, while H_2SO_4, with the most number of oxygen atoms, is named sulfuric acid. Nitrogen is another element that forms two oxyacids, HNO_2 and HNO_3.

Chlorine forms four oxyacids with chemical formulas $HClO$, $HClO_2$, $HClO_3$, and $HClO_4$. To name aqueous solutions of $HClO$, $HClO_2$, $HClO_3$, and $HClO_4$ the various prefixes and suffixes given above are added to the "chlor" stem followed by the word acid. As a result, $HClO$ with one oxygen atom, i.e., the least number of oxygen atoms, is named hypochlorous acid. $HClO_2$ with two oxygen atoms is named chlorous acid. $HClO_3$ with three oxygen atoms is named chloric acid. $HClO_4$ with four oxygen atoms, i.e., the most number of oxygen atoms, is named perchloric acid. All of the elements in Group VIIA, except fluorine, form this same series of four oxyacids, i.e., iodine forms the four oxyacids HIO, HIO_2, HIO_3, and HIO_4.

Using the above rules, name the following oxyacids:

$HBrO_2$(aq) __69__ $HBrO$(aq) __71__ HIO_3(aq) __73__

HIO_4(aq) __70__ HNO_3(aq) __72__ HNO_2(aq) __74__

Nomenclature of Polyatomic Ions

Although it is best to memorize the names for the more common polyatomic ions, this memorization process is aided by an understanding of the origin of the polyatomic ion. Most polyatomic ions are derived from oxyacids by loss of proton(s), H1. For example, the polyatomic ion sulfite is derived from the oxyacid sulfurous acid by loss of two H1, as shown below.

$$H_2SO_3 \rightarrow SO_3^{-2} + 2\,H^+ \qquad \textbf{"-ous"} \rightarrow \textbf{"-ite"}$$

sulfurous acid   *sulfite*

Notice that the "-ous" ending of the oxyacid is changed to "-ite" in the polyatomic ion. Likewise, the polyatomic ion sulfate is derived from the oxyacid sulfuric acid by loss of two H1, as shown below.

$$H_2SO_4 \rightarrow SO_4^{-2} + 2\,H^+ \qquad \textbf{"-ic"} \rightarrow \textbf{"-ate"}$$

sulfuric acid   *sulfate*

Notice that the "-ic" ending of the oxyacid acid is changed to "-ate" in the polyatomic ion. If a diprotic acid, such as H2SO3, loses only one proton, then the prefix "bi-" or the word "hydrogen" is added to the name of the polyatomic ion as shown below.

$$H_2SO_3 \qquad \rightarrow \qquad HSO_3^- \qquad + \qquad H^+$$

sulfurous acid   *bisulfite or hydrogen sulfite*

Accordingly, NO_2^-, which is derived from the oxyacid nitrous acid, HNO_2, is named ___75___ while NO_3^-, which is derived from the oxyacid nitric acid, HNO_3, is named ___76___. ClO_4^-, which is derived from the oxyacid perchloric acid, $HClO_4$, is named ___77___ while ClO^-, which is derived from the oxyacid hypochlorous acid, $HClO$, is named ___78___. CO_3^{-2} and HCO_3^-, which are derived from the oxyacid carbonic acid, H_2CO^3, are named ___79___ and ___80___, respectively.

Common Names

Common or trivial names are used for some compounds. Although many chemicals have common names, a list of those common names normally encountered in freshman chemistry is given below. As outlined in the preceding sections, give the IUPAC name for each compound below. Before naming, remember to first classify the compound as ionic or molecular.

Compound	Common Name	IUPAC Name
H_2O	water	___81___
NH_3	ammonia	___82___
PH_3	phosphine	___83___
N_2H_4	hydrazine	___84___
CaO	lime	___85___
$Ca(OH)_2$	slaked lime	___86___
Na_2CO_3	soda ash	___87___
BH_3	borane	___88___
Fe_2O_3	rust	___89___

Self-Test

In naming binary compounds, ionic and molecular, the name of the more __90__ element is written first, followed by the name of the more __91__ element. The ending of the second element named is replaced by the suffix __92__. Greek prefixes are used in naming __93__ compounds. Using the old system to distinguish ionic compounds containing metal cations of variable charge, the ending of the metal is replaced by the suffix __94__ or __95__ dependent on the charge of the metal. The metal of __96__ charge is denoted with the "-ous" suffix, while the metal of __97__ charge is denoted with the "-ic" suffix. Using the IUPAC or Stock system, the charge of the metal is denoted with a __98__ after the name of the metal. When deriving the chemical formula of an ionic compound (also called the formula unit) from the name, the chemical formula must be __99__ such that the total number of positive and negative charges are equal.

Some binary hydrides are acidic when dissolved in water and are called __100__. Such acids are denoted by the prefix __101__, followed by the suffix __102__, and the word __103__. Phosphoric acid, H_3PO_4, is an example of a(n) __104__. When phosphoric acid loses three protons, the polyatomic ion __105__ is formed. This polyatomic ion is named __106__.

Classify (ionic, molecular, binary acid, oxyacid) and name each of the following compounds:

	Classification	Name		Classification	Name
HI(g)	107	108	SF_4	123	124
HI(aq)	109	110	$HBrO_4$	125	126
$AlBr_3$	111	112	I_2O_5	127	128
CoI_3	113	114	HCl(aq)	129	130
$CoCl_2$	115	116	$HClO_3$	131	132
HIO_2	117	118	BaS	133	134
NH_4Cl	119	120	FeS	135	136
$Mg(OH)_2$	121	122	$Fe(ClO_3)_3$	137	138

Write chemical formulas for the following compounds:

	Chemical Formula		Chemical Formula
iron(III)sulfide	139	xenon trioxide	144
iron(II)phosphate	140	hydrosulfuric acid	145
stannous nitride	141	sulfuric acid	146
stannic nitrate	142	sodium sulfite	147
dichlorine heptoxide	143	potassium sulfate	148

Appendix C – Chemical Nomenclature

Introduction

1. _____   4. _____   7. _____

2. _____   5. _____   8. _____

3. _____   6. _____   9. _____

Nomenclature of Ionic Compounds

10. _____   22. _____   34. _____

11. _____   23. _____   35. _____

12. _____   24. _____   36. _____

13. _____   25. _____   37. _____

14. _____   26. _____   38. _____

15. _____   27. _____   39. _____

16. _____   28. _____   40. _____

17. _____   29. _____

18. _____   30. _____

19. _____   31. _____

20. _____   32. _____

21. _____   33. _____

Chemical Formula for Chemical Name

41. _____

42. _____

43. _____

44. _____

45. _____

46. _____

47. _____

48. _____

Nomenclature of Molecular Compounds

49. _____

50. _____

51. _____

52. _____

53. _____

54. _____

55. _____

56. _____

57. _____

58. _____

59. _____

60. _____

61. _____

62. _____

63. _____

64. _____

Nomenclature of Binary Acids, Binary Hydrides, & OxyAcids

65. _____

66. _____

67. _____

68. _____

69. _____

70. _____

71. _____

72. _____

73. _____

74. _____

Nomenclature of Polyatomic Ions

75. _____

76. _____

77. _____

78. _____

79. _____

80. _____

81. _____

Common Names

82. _____

83. _____

84. _____

85. _____

86. _____

87. _____

88. _____

89. _____

Self Test

90. _____

91. _____

92. _____

93. _____

94. _____

95. _____

96. _____

97. _____

98. _____

99. _____

100. _____

101. _____

102. _____

103. _____

104. _____

105. _____

106. _____

107. _____

108. _____

109. _____

110. _____

111. _____

112. _____

113. _____

114. _____

115. _____

116. _____

117. _____

118. _____

119. _____

120. _____

121. _____

122. _____

123. _____

124. _____

125. _____

126. _____

127. _____

128. _____

129. _____

130. _____

131. _____

132. _____

133. _____

134. _____

135. _____

136. _____

137. _____

138. _____

139. _____

140. _____

141. _____

142. _____

143. _____

144. _____

145. _____

146. _____

147. _____

148. _____

Appendix D – Solubility Rules

The solubility rules given below are for *ionic compounds* or *salts*. Therefore, these rules do not apply to molecular compounds such as acids (e.g., HCl, H_2S, H_2SO_4, $HC_2H_3O_2$, etc.) or organic compounds (e.g., C_2H_5OH). A *soluble ionic compound* dissolves to a significant extent in water and is generally defined as having a solubility in water of > 0.1 M. An *insoluble ionic compound* does not dissolve to a significant extent in water and is generally defined as having a solubility in water of < 0.1 M. Please note that the 0.1 M dividing line between soluble and insoluble is a man-made rule (i.e., not a fundamental law of nature). Therefore, ionic compounds with intermediate solubilities (i.e., near the 0.1 M limit) may be classified as soluble in one source but insoluble in another source. In this presentation, ionic compounds with intermediate solubilities will be specified as *sparingly soluble*.

Use the solubility rules in the order given. Once a rule is found that applies to either the anion or the cation of a salt, do not proceed further through the rules. Use that rule to predict the solubility of a salt.

Solubility Rules for Ionic Compounds (Salts) in Water

1. Ionic compounds that contain **Group IA metal cations** (Na^+, K^+, Li^+, etc.) or **ammonium cations, NH_4^+**, are **soluble**.

2. Ionic compounds that contain NO_3^-, NO_2^-, ClO_3^-, ClO_4^-, $C_2H_3O_2^-$, or HCO_3^- anions are **soluble**. (Note: $AgNO_2$ is sparingly soluble.)

3. Ionic compounds that contain Cl^-, Br^-, or I^- anions are **soluble except** when combined with Ag^+, Hg_2^{2+}, or Pb_2^+ cations.

4. Ionic compounds that contain SO_4^{2-} anions are **soluble except** when combined with Ag^+, Hg_2^{2+}, Pb^{2+}, Ba^{2+}, Ca^{2+}, or Sr^{2+} cations. (Note: Ag_2SO_4 and $CaSO_4$ are sparingly soluble.)

5. Most ionic compounds that contain S^{2-} anions are **insoluble** except when combined with a Group IA or IIA metal cation or NH_4^+.

6. Most ionic compounds that contain OH^-, O^{2-}, CO_3^{2-}, PO_4^{3-}, CrO_4^{2-}, or $Cr_2O_7^{2-}$ anions are **insoluble** except when combined with a Group IA metal cation or NH_4^+. Note: $Ca(OH)_2$, $Sr(OH)_2$, and $Ba(OH)_2$ are sparingly soluble but are strong bases and therefore strong electrolytes when dissolved.

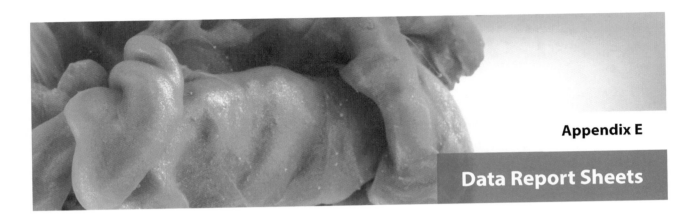

Experiment 1: Synthesis of Nanoparticles: Ferrofluids

_____ AM or PM

Lab Room No.   _Desk No._   _Lab Day_   _Time (Circle One)_

_____

Student Name

TEACHING ASSISTANT USE ONLY

EXPERIMENT 1 GRADE _____ %

- Did the student do the entire procedure and obtain a product?   Yes _____   No _____
- Is the resulting product magnetic (i.e., a ferrofluid)?   Yes _____   No _____
- If not, did the student give a valid explanation for why the   Yes _____   No _____
  product was not magnetic?
- What was the explanation?

The teaching assistant will sign below once satisfied that the student has performed the entire procedure. The report will not be accepted or graded unless signed.

Teaching Assistant's Approval: _____
                                                    Signature

---

Experiment 2: Analysis of Density

AM or PM

Lab Room No.   Desk No.   Lab Day   Time (Circle One)

Student Name

Table 2.1: Density Determinations

Material	Mass of Displaced Water (g)	Mass of Sample (g)	Volume of Sample (mL)	Density of Material (g/mL)
PVC (polyvinyl Chloride)				
Copper				
Brass				
Aluminum				
Pyrex glass				

Show a complete sample calculation here. Use your own data and be sure to include units and appropriate significant figures.

TEACHING ASSISTANT USE ONLY

EXPERIMENT 2 GRADE _____ %

The teaching assistant will sign below once satisfied that the student has performed the entire procedure. The report will not be accepted or graded unless signed.

Teaching Assistant's Approval: _____
                                                 Signature

Experiment 3: Oxalate Stoichiometry

AM or PM

Lab Room No.   Desk No.   Lab Day   Time (Circle One)

Student Name

Table 3.1: Synthesis of Metal Oxalate

Data	Result
Chemical formula of your hydrated metal salt	
Mass of hydrated metal salt used	
Volume of oxalic acid solution used	
Mass of oxalic acid	
Mass of weigh dish + contents	
Mass of empty weigh dish	
Mass if filter paper	
Actual yield of hydrated metal oxalate precipitate	
Color of hydrated metal oxalate precipitate	
Limiting reactant (either hydrated metal salt or oxalic acid)	
Theoretical yield of hydrated metal oxalate product	
Percent yield of hydrated metal oxalate product	

Table 3.2: Pyrolysis of Metal Oxalate

Data	Result
Before pyrolysis: mass of dish plus hydrated metal oxalate	
Mass of empty aluminum dish	
Before pyrolysis: mass of hydrated metal oxalate	
After pyrolysis: final mass of dish plus pyrolysis product	
After pyrolysis: actual mass of pyrolysis product	
Color of pyrolysis product	
From prelab (quest. #5): theoretical mass of product in rxn A	
From prelab (quest. #5): theoretical mass of product in rxn B	
From prelab (quest. #5): theoretical mass of product in rxn C	
Using the above information, decide which of the three possible pyrolysis reactions actually occurred, rxn, A, B, or C?	
Chemical formula of the metal containing pyrolysis product from chosen rxn, A, B, or C?	

Continued on reverse.

Show your calculations to step 12 of Part I here.

TEACHING ASSISTANT USE ONLY

EXPERIMENT 3 GRADE _____ %

- Did the student have the appropriate set of prelab questions   Yes _____   No _____
  completed before lab?

The teaching assistant will sign below once satisfied that the student has performed the entire procedure. The report will not be accepted or graded unless signed.

Teaching Assistant's Approval: _____
                                                            Signature

Experiment 4: Vitamin Analysis

AM or PM
Time (Circle One)

Lab Room No.   Desk No.   Lab Day

Student Name

Sample Number _____

Mass of Powdered Tablet Used _____

Table 4.1: Analysis of Standard.

Standard	Results
$[Fe^{3+}]$ in original (see label)	
Absorbance of your standard solution	
$[Fe^{3+}]$ in your standard solution	
ratio of $[Fe^{3+}]_{std.soln.}$/Absorbance	

Table 4.2: Analysis of Vitamin Tablet Sample.

Solution	Absorbance	$[Fe^{3+}]$ (M)
1		
2		
3		
4		
5		
6		

Table 4.3: Data Analysis

Solution	Data
$[Fe^{3+}]$ in Solution 1	
Total mass of Fe^{3+} in Solution 1 (g)	
Mass % of Fe in vitamin tablet	

Continued on reverse.

EXPERIMENT 4 GRADE _____ %

The teaching assistant will sign below once satisfied that the student has performed the entire procedure. The report will not be accepted or graded unless signed.

Teaching Assistant's Approval: _____
Signature

Experiment 5: Chemicals in the Home

Lab Room No.   Desk No.   Lab Day   Time (Circle One)

Student Name

Observations

a. Unknown solid + conc. H_2SO_4?   _____

b. Confirmatory tests and results?   _____

_____

_____

_____

_____

_____

c. Unknown ion?   _____

TEACHING ASSISTANT USE ONLY

EXPERIMENT 5 GRADE _____ %

The teaching assistant will sign below once satisfied that the student has performed the entire procedure. The report will not be accepted or graded unless signed.

Teaching Assistant's Approval: _____
Signature

Experiment 6: Water Hardness

Lab Room No.   Desk No.   Lab Day   Time (Circle One)

Student Name

Report your two best titrations for your unknown and circle the answer that you think is best.

Titrations		Unknown	
		1	2
9	Volume of unknown titrated		
12	Volume of EDTA solution used		
13	Concentration of EDTA solution	_____ mL EDTA solution = _____ mg CaCO$_3$	
14	mg of CaCO$_3$ in the sample		
16	ppm CaCO$_3$ in sample = mg of CaCO$_3$ per L of sample or mg of CaCO$_3$ per 1000 g sample		

TEACHING ASSISTANT USE ONLY

EXPERIMENT 6 GRADE _____ %

The teaching assistant will sign below once satisfied that the student has performed the entire procedure. The report will not be accepted or graded unless signed.

Teaching Assistant's Approval: _____
                                              Signature

Experiment 7: The Kool-Aid Acid Test

Lab Room No.	Desk No.	Lab Day	AM or PM Time (Circle One)

Student Name

Table 7-5: Generic Drink Mix Sample: Data

Drink Mix Sample Type	Mass of Mix in Your 1/4 Packet (g)	Volume 1/4 Packet Mix Was Diluted to (mL)

Table 7-6: Generic Drink Mix: Calculations and Results

Molarity of NaOH Solution Used

Calculations and Results	End Point Found by Color Change	
	Trial 1	Trial 2
volume of drink mix titrated		
mass of drink mix in volume titrated		
buret reading at end point		
inital buret reading		
volume of NaOH delivered to reach end point		
moles of citric acid		
mass of citric acid in volume of drink mix titrated		
% citric acid in drink mix		

Which drink mix has more acid content, the Kool-Aid brand or the generic drink mix?

C. CALCULATIONS AND ANALYSIS - TITRATION CURVE

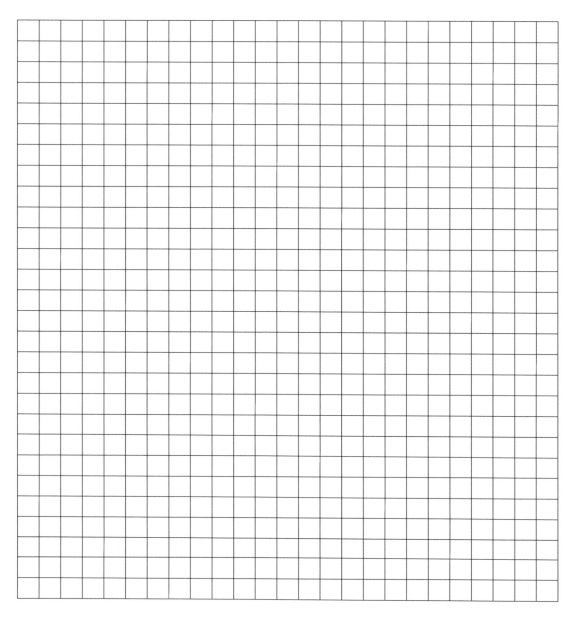

Experiment 8: Halogens and Halides: Activity Series

_____

AM or PM

Lab Room No.   _Desk No._   _Lab Day_   _Time (Circle One)_

_____

Student Name

Part I: Precipitation and Redox Reactions

Observations

a.   Unknown + $AgNO_3$(aq)?   _____

b.   Unknown + $Ca(NO_3)_2$(aq)?   _____

c.   Unknown + Cl_2(aq)?   _____

d.   Unknown + Br_2(aq)?   _____

Part II: Reaction of the Halides with Sulfuric Acid

a.   Unknown + H_2SO_4?   _____

_____

_____

_____

Part III: Unknown

Halide Ion Present in Unknown?   _____

TEACHING ASSISTANT USE ONLY

EXPERIMENT 8 GRADE _____ %

The teaching assistant will sign below once satisfied that the student has performed the entire procedure. The report will not be accepted or graded unless signed.

Teaching Assistant's Approval: _____

Signature

Experiment 9: Thermochemistry to the Rescue

AM or PM

Lab Room No.   Desk No.   Lab Day   Time (Circle One)

Student Name

Part I: Frostbite—Approximation of Specific Heat of Human Hand

Table 9.1: Sausage Thermochemistry.

Data	Unit	Result
Mass of the water($d_{water} = 1.00g/mL$)	g	
T_i, initial Temperature of water	°C	
T_f, Final Temperature of water	°C	
Heat removed/lost from the water	J	
Heat absorbed by the sausage	J	
Mass of the sausage	g	
T_i, initial Temperature of water	°C	
T_f, Final Temperature of water	°C	
Specific heat of the sausage	$J \cdot g^{-1} °C^{-1}$	

Part II: Portable Heat Pack Thermodynamics

Table 9.2: Observations of Salt Dissolution.

Observations	NaCl	KCl	CaCl$_2$
Temperature change (warmer, colder, neither)?			
Dissolution is endothermic or exothermic?			

Table 9.3: CaCl$_2$ Dissolution Thermochemistry.

Observation	Unit	1st Run (100 mL water)	2nd Run (70 mL water)	3rd Run (50 mL water)
Mass of CaCl$_2$	g			
Volume of water	mL			
Mass of initial soln	g			
T$_i$, initial Temperature of water	°C			
T$_f$, final Temperature of water	°C			
ΔT	°C			
Heat absorbed/gained by the solution	J			
Heat produced/lost by the reaction	J			
ΔH$_{rxn}$	J·g^{-1}			
$\dfrac{\text{mass CaCl}_2}{\text{mass water}}$	ratio			

Part III: Development of a Heat Pack

Table 9.4: Heat Pack Calculations.

Data	Unit	Result
Volume of your hand	sausage	
Mass of your hand	g	
Heat required to raise temperature	J	
Amount of CaCl$_2$ required	g	
Ideal CaCl$_2$: water mass ratio	ratio	

Evaluation of heat pack perfomance (i.e., Did it work and give a temperature change of 22-25 °C? How would you make it better?):

Table 9.5: Proposed Heat Pack Recipe

Data	Result
Mass of CaCl$_2$	
Volume of water	
Target temperature change	

TEACHING ASSISTANT USE ONLY

EXPERIMENT 9 GRADE _____ %

The teaching assistant will sign below once satisfied that the student has performed the entire procedure. The report will not be accepted or graded unless signed.

Teaching Assistant's Approval: _____
                                                    Signature

Experiment 10: VSEPR Theory: Shapes of Molecules

Lab Room No.   Desk No.   Lab Day   <u>AM or PM</u>
Time (Circle One)

Student Name

Species AX$_2$, AX$_3$, AX$_4$, AX$_5$, and AX$_6$

A. NO LONE PAIRS OF ELECTRONS.
___(A = CENTRAL ATOM, X = BONDED ATOMS)

1. **Consider the species BeF$_2$ (Ex. AX$_2$).** Draw a Lewis structure, make a 3-D model, and show these below. The F-Be-F bond angle in the BeF$_2$ molecule is _____.

    BeF$_2$ Lewis Structure: **3-D Model:**

2. **Consider the species BF$_3$ (Ex. AX$_3$).** Draw a Lewis structure, make a 3-D model, and show these below. All of the F atoms are in the _____ (same/different) plane. The bond angles in this molecule are _____ degrees. All of the B-F bonds in BF$_3$ _____ (would/would not) be polar. Since the F atoms are the same, the molecule _____ (would/would not) be polar.

    BF$_3$ Lewis Structure: **3-D Model:**

    a. BF$_2$Cl molecule _____ (would/would not) be polar because _____.

3. **Consider the species CF₄ (Ex. AX₄).** Draw a Lewis structure, make a 3-D model, and show these below. The bond angles in this molecule are _____ degrees. Since all F atoms are the same, this molecule _____ (would/would not) be polar.

CF₄ Lewis Structure: **3-D Model:**

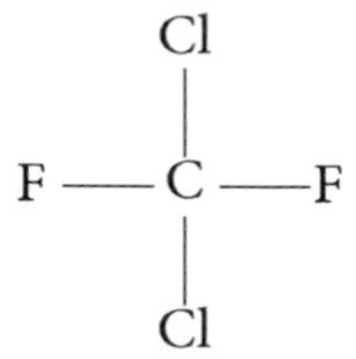

F —— C —— F   The CCl₃F molecule _____ (would/would not) be polar. Is CCl₂F₂ (Lewis structure shown to the left) polar? _____.
Tell why or why not. _____.

```
      Cl
      |
F —— C —— F
      |
      Cl
```

4. **Consider the species PF₅ (Ex. AX₅).** Draw a Lewis structure, make a 3-D model, and show these below. In this species, the 2-5, 3-5, and 4-5 bonds are in the/a _____ (same, different) plane. The other two bonds, 1-5 and 5-6, are called out-of-plane and are _____ to this plane. The in-plane angles are _____ degrees. The out-of-plane bonds make an angle of _____ degrees with the in-plane bonds. The _____ and _____ out-of-plane bonds are longer than the 2-5, 3-5, and 4-5 in-plane bonds because

_____.

PF₅ Lewis Structure: **3-D Model:**

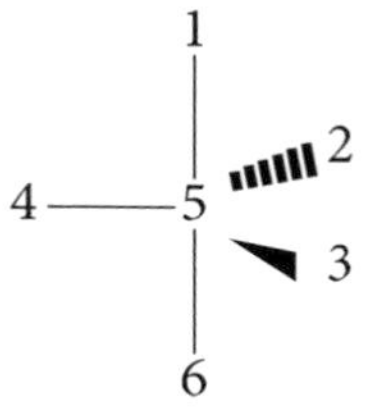

5. **Consider the species SF₆ (Ex. AX₆).** Draw a Lewis structure, make a model, and show these below. All of the bonds in this species are equal in length. All of the bond angles in the molecule are _____ degrees. All of the edges of a regular octahedron _____ (are/are not) equal in length.

SF₆ Lewis Structure: **3-D Model:**

```
    1
    |
    |
4 —— 5 ••••• 2
    | ◥ 3
    |
    6
```

The F and Cl atoms in SF_4Cl_2 can be arranged in two different ways to give two different models (or geometric isomers). Use two colored plastic pieces and four differently colored plastic pieces to make two different models of SF_4Cl_2. Draw these two different models below. The two different models of SF_4Cl_2 are called geometric isomers. One isomer is called the *cis*- (Latin: on this side) and the other the *trans*- (Latin: across) isomer. Thus, in the *cis*-isomer the two Cl atoms are on the same side of the molecule, while in the *trans*-isomer the two Cl atoms are on opposite sides of the molecule.

cis 3-D Geometric Isomer of SF_4Cl_2:　　　　　　**trans 3-D Geometric Isomer of SF_4Cl_2:**

Of the SF_4Cl_2 geometric isomers, the _____ (*cis/trans*) isomer would be polar.

B. LONE PAIRS OF ELECTRONS.
(A=CENTRAL ATOM, X=BONDED ATOMS, U=LONE PAIR OF ELECTRONS)

1. **Variations on AX_3: AX_2U (bent).** Draw Lewis structures and make models of BF_3 and BF_2^-. Draw the Lewis structures and three-dimensional models below. Show the location of atoms and any lone pairs of electrons. Name the molecular shape of each.

　　Lewis Structure:　　　　**BF_3 3-D Model:**　　　**Name of Molecular Shape:**

BF_3

　　Lewis Structure:　　　　**BF_2^- 3-D Model:**　　　**Name of Molecular Shape:**

BF_2^-

The molecular shape of the BF_2^- ion is _____ (linear, bent) because

_____.

Is the BP-BP angle in BF_2^- equal to 120°? _____ Why or why not?

_____.

2. **Variations on AX₄: AX₃U (trigonal pyramidal) and AX₂U₂ (bent).** In placing four objects on a sphere, to get them as far apart as possible, they would be placed on the largest tetrahedron that could be placed within the sphere. Lone pairs are not picked up by the various experimental methods, but their positions are surmised from the shapes of molecules and bond angles. Draw Lewis structures and make models of NH_3, PCl_3, AsH_3, and CH_3^-. Show 3-D models and Lewis structures below and on the next page. Show the location of atoms and any lone pairs of electrons. Name the molecular shape of each.

NH_3

Lewis Structure: NH_3 3-D Model: Name of Molecular Shape:

PCl_2

Lewis Structure: PCl_3 3-D Model: Name of Molecular Shape:

AsH_3

Lewis Structure: AsH_3 3-D Model: Name of Molecular Shape:

CH_3^-

Lewis Structure: CH_3^- 3-D Model: Name of Molecular Shape:

Draw Lewis structures and make models of H_2O, NH_2^-, and CCl_2^{-2}. Draw the Lewis structures and three-dimensional models below. Show the location of atoms and any lone pairs of electrons. Name the molecular shape of each.

H_2O

Lewis Structure: H_2O 3-D Model: Name of Molecular Shape:

Lewis Structure: NH_2^- 3-D Model: **Name of Molecular Shape:**

NH_2^-

Lewis Structure: CCl_2^{-2} 3-D Model: **Name of Molecular Shape:**

CCl_2^{-2}

How does one account for the fact that the bond angles in H_2O are smaller (~105°) than those in NH_3 (~107°)?

The most repulsive type of electron pair interaction is _____ (BP-BP, BP-LP, or LP-LP). Which will occupy the largest volume, a lone pair or a bonding pair of electrons? Why?

3. **Variations on AX_5: AX_4U (seesaw), AX_3U_2 (T-shaped), and AX_2U_3 (linear).** Draw a Lewis structure, make a 3-D model, and name the molecular shape of PCl_5. Show the location of atoms and any lone pairs of electrons. Name the molecular shape.

    Lewis Structure: PCl_5 3-D Model: **Name of Molecular Shape:**

PCl_5

Draw a Lewis structure for PCl_4^- (below). Show the location of atoms and any lone pairs of electrons. In PCl_4^-, the lone pair of electrons can be placed in either an equatorial or an axial position. Determine the total number of each type of 90° repulsive interaction for each placement.

PLACEMENT OF LONE PAIR

I. Equatorial

II. Axial

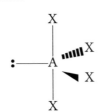
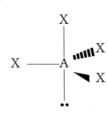

Number of each type of 90° repulsive interaction in each:

90° LP-LP	_____	_____
90° LP-BP	_____	_____
90° BP-BP	_____	_____

In terms of increasing repulsions between electron pairs, the trend is: BP-BP (least repulsive) > BP-LP > LP-LP (most repulsive). In order to minimize repulsions between electron pairs situated 90° apart, the lone pair of electrons should be placed _____ (equatorial, axial). Show the correct 3-D model and molecular shape name for PCl_4^- below.

Lewis Structure: **PCl_4^- 3-D Model:**   **Name of Molecular Shape:**

PCl_4

Draw a Lewis structure of ClF_3. Show the location of atoms and any lone pairs of electrons. In ClF_3, the two lone pairs of electrons can be placed one axial and one equatorial, both equatorial, or both axial. Determine the total number of each type of 90° repulsive interaction for each placement.

PLACEMENT OF TWO LONE PAIRS

I. Axial/Equatorial   II. Equatorial   III. Axial

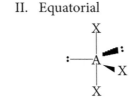
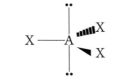

Number of each type of 90° repulsive interaction in each:

90° LP-LP	_____	_____	_____
90° LP-BP	_____	_____	_____
90° BP-BP	_____	_____	_____

In order to minimize repulsions between electron pairs situated 90° apart, the two lone pairs of electrons should be placed _____. Show the correct 3-D model and molecular shape name for ClF₃ below.

Lewis Structure: **ClF₃ 3-D Model:**   **Name of Molecular Shape:**

ClF₄

Draw a Lewis structure of I_3^-. Show the location of atoms and any lone pairs of electrons. In I_3^-, the three lone pairs of electrons can be placed all equatorial, one axial and two equatorial, or two axial and one equatorial. Determine the total number of each type of 90° repulsive interaction for each placement.

PLACEMENT OF THREE LONE PAIRS

I. Equatorial   II. One Axial/Two Equatorial   III. Two Axial/One Equatorial

Number of each type of 90° repulsive interaction in each:

90° LP-LP _____   _____   _____
90° LP-BP _____   _____   _____
90° BP-BP _____   _____   _____

In order to minimize repulsions between electron pairs situated 90° apart, the three lone pairs of electrons should be placed _____. Show the correct 3-D model and molecular shape name for I_3^-.

Lewis Structure: **PCl₅ 3-D Model:**   **Name of Molecular Shape:**

I₃⁻

4. **Variations on AX₆: AX₅U (square pyramidal) and AX₄U₂ (square planar).** Draw Lewis structures and make models of SF₆ and SF₅⁻. Show the location of atoms and any lone pairs of electrons. Name the molecular shape of each.

Lewis Structure: **SF₆ 3-D Model:**   **Name of Molecular Shape:**

SF₆

	Lewis Structure:	**SF_5^- 3-D Model:**	**Name of Molecular Shape:**

SF_5

In SF_5^-, does it matter where the lone pair of electrons is placed? _____ Why or why not? _____

Draw a Lewis structure for XeF_4. Show the location of atoms and any lone pairs of electrons. In XeF_4, the two lone pairs of electrons can be placed in opposite or adjacent positions. Determine the total number of each type of 90° repulsive interaction for each placement.

PLACEMENT OF TWO LONE PAIRS

I. Opposite

II. Adjacent

Number of each type of 90° repulsive interaction in each:

90° LP-LP	_____	_____
90° LP-BP	_____	_____
90° BP-BP	_____	_____

In order to minimize repulsions between electron pairs situated 90° apart, the two lone pairs of electrons should be placed in positions. Show the correct 3-D model and molecular shape name for XeF_4 below.

	Lewis Structure:	**XeF_4 3-D Model:**	**Name of Molecular Shape:**

XeF_4

5. **Practice Molecules and Ions.** Draw Lewis structures, make models, draw three-dimensional shapes, and name the molecular shapes of the following:

CH_3Cl $TeCl_4$ XeF_3^+

SCl_2 IF_5 H_3O^+

OF_2 ICl_4^- $XeOF_4$

TEACHING ASSISTANT USE ONLY

EXPERIMENT 10 GRADE _____ %

The teaching assistant will sign below once satisfied that the student has performed the entire procedure. The report will not be accepted or graded unless signed.

Teaching Assistant's Approval: _____
                                                            Signature

Experiment 11: The Reason for Biodeisel

_____

Lab Room No.   _Desk No._   _Lab Day_

AM or PM

Time (Circle One)

_____

Student Name

Part I: Biodiesel Synthesis

Table 11.1: Evaporation.

Compound	T_i (°C)	T_f (°C)	ΔT (°C)
Pentane (C_5H_{12})			
Octane (C_8H_{18})			
Dodecane ($C_{12}H_{26}$)			
Ethanol (C_2H_5OH)			
Propanol (C_3H_7OH)			
Butanol (C_4H_9OH)			

Table 11.2: Viscosity.

Compound	Time
Ethanol	
Propanol	
Butanol	
Octanol ($C_8H_{17}OH$)	
Pentane	
Octane	
Dodecane	

Table 11.3: Viscosity.

Compound	Time
Biodiesel	
Oil	

Part II: Relative Rates of Evaporation

Answer the following questions using complete sentences for explanations. Use results from your experiment to support your statements and fully explain the intermolecular forces present in each liquid. Discuss relative strengths of intermolecular forces and how these forces affect physical properties of evaporation and viscosity.

1. Consider your ΔT values for pentane, octane, and dodecane in Table 11-1. Arrange these according to increasing ΔT value. Use your knowledge of intermolecular forces in these three liquids to fully explain your observed trend.

2. Consider your ΔT values for ethanol, propanol, and butanol in Table 11-1. Arrange these according to increasing ΔT value. Use your knowledge of intermolecular forces to fully explain your observed trend.

3. Consider your time values for the viscosity experiment for octanol, pentane, and octane in Table 11-2. Arrange these according to increasing time. Use your knowledge of intermolecular forces to fully explain your observed trend.

4. Consider the time values for the viscosity experiment for oil and biodiesel in Table 11-3. Refer back to the chemical structures of oil and biodiesel on page 114. Use your knowledge of intermolecular forces to fully explain why oil is more viscous than biodiesel.